Atlas of IC Technologies:

An Introduction to VLSI Processes

W. Maly

Electrical and Computer Engineering Department
Carnegie-Mellon University

The Benjamin/Cummings Publishing Company, Inc.
Menlo Park, California • Reading, Massachusetts
Don Mills, Ontario • Wokingham, U.K. • Amsterdam
Sydney • Singapore • Tokyo • Madrid • Bogota
Santiago • San Juan

Sponsoring Editor: Craig Bartholomew
Developmental and Copy Editor: Martine Westermann
Production Supervisor: Kristina Montague
Cover Design: Victoria Ann Philp

Library of Congress Cataloguing-in-Publication Data

Maly, W.
    Atlas of IC technologies.

    Includes bibliographies and index.
    1. Integrated circuits--Very large scale
integration--Design and construction. I. Title.
TK7874.M254 1987   621.381'73   87-8083
ISBN 0-8053-6850-7

CDEFGHIJ-HA-898

The Benjamin/Cummings Publishing Company, Inc.
2727 Sand Hill Road
Menlo Park, California 94025

I dedicate this book
to my friends, students, and faculty
of Technical University of Warsaw.

Preface

VLSI semiconductor houses, small and large, have to treat circuit design and process development as more or less separate domains, partly because of tradition and partly out of the need for management efficiency. As a result, design and process development are usually performed by different groups of engineers reporting to different managers. Over the years, as design has increasingly focused on the entire system rather than on single devices, and as process development has drifted towards equipment-related issues, the organizational split has further and further separated design and process development activities. Eventually, two different VLSI orientations evolved--a system orientation and a process orientation.

Engineers with a system point of view generally would like to see VLSI design as a more or less geometrical activity. Some process-oriented individuals, on the other hand, tend to see process enhancements as the only effective means of achieving improvements in the manufacturing cost and performance of VLSI circuits. Consequently, the communication between these two worlds -- one in which a transistor is seen as a *"common part of a green and red box"* and the other in which the same transistor is seen as *"an outcome of an extremely complex and still not fully understood phenomenon"* -- is not as effective as it should be when VLSI circuits have to be designed faster and fabricated more cheaply. Therefore, filling the growing gap between the system and process worlds seems crucial for the future of the entire VLSI area.

There are several different ways to improve communications between the design and process VLSI orientations. Naturally, adequate education is the most obvious solution, and it is already being provided in both industry and academia. Industry offers employee training courses for this purpose. In the colleges and universities, standard electrical engineering courses are gradually modified to address modern VLSI problems. The circuit-oriented courses are taught with more and more emphasis on VLSI processes, while the technology-oriented courses are starting to discuss device, layout, and circuit-related issues. Because of time constraints, such modifications are usually introduced in the form of supplementary material that enhances the treatment in the main textbook for the course with some VLSI topics. This *Atlas of IC Technologies* provides such supplementary material. It should be useful in a number of courses where traditional texts should be supported with basic information about modern VLSI processes and basic concepts of process integration.

The initial concept for the Atlas was tested in the standard microelectronics course at Carnegie-Mellon University in the spring of 1986 and 1987. The undergraduate junior-level course, taught with the main textbook by Hodges and Jackson, was chosen for this purpose. During the course a large set of drawings in the form of handouts and overhead transparencies was used to teach students about bipolar, NMOS, and CMOS processes. The goal was to illustrate relationships between the physics of the process, the geometry of an IC layout, and the electrical parameters of the IC components. This information was used to explain basic features of circuit integration in a typical circuit-oriented course.

The results were very encouraging. After the first three weeks, a large majority of the students was able to interpret and understand bipolar, NMOS, and CMOS layouts. The concept of parasitic capacitances and other elements needed to determine values of, for instance, SPICE model parameters were clearly understood and correctly estimated from simple layout examples. Finally, a majority of the students was able to draw cross-sectional views of cells from sample layouts. The same handouts were also popular among graduate students in the traditional VLSI design courses.

This classroom experience indicates that VLSI processes can be taught in the undergraduate and graduate system and circuit-oriented courses. It also suggests that modification of these traditional microelectronics courses is possible without removing any basic components from the courses. This can be achieved within the time constraints of the course, provided that the material is presented mainly in a pictorial manner and that IC devices are shown as three-dimensional structures created by a precisely defined sequence of processing steps. The above observations led to the effort that resulted in this book, which through 3D pictures introduces all basic technologies, including advanced VLSI processes.

This Atlas is intended to be a supplement to the textbooks used in circuit and system-oriented courses as well as technology-oriented courses. More specifically, the material presented in this book should be useful:

- In the **undergraduate digital and analog circuit courses**;
- In the **graduate VLSI design course**;
- In the graduate **VLSI process-related courses**; and
- In **employee training courses** where system-oriented professionals can refresh their knowledge about VLSI processes.

In the first part of this book, 3D drawings illustrating basic processing steps and basic features of the bipolar, NMOS, and CMOS technologies are presented. The second part of the book examines more advanced processes. The full-page figures are accompanied by explanatory text on the facing pages.

The first part of the book comprises Chapters 1, 2, 3, 4, and 5. Chapter 1 describes process operations. Chapter 2 addresses the relationship between processing errors, random process instabilities, and geometrical design rules. Chapter 3 is a very important chapter, describing standard junction-isolated bipolar technology and discussing the basic characteristics of the bipolar elements. This chapter is important because bipolar technology, despite its age, is an excellent vehicle to illustrate the basic concept of integration and the limitations in IC device performance resulting from the nature of the process. Chapter 4 describes the simple (Mead-Conway style) NMOS process. The explanation considers processing steps, features of the transistors, and various parasitic elements. Chapter 5 shows the simple n-well CMOS process in a similar manner.

Chapters 6 through 11 form the second part of the book, discussing more advanced processes. In these chapters 3D drawings are replaced by more conventional illustrations and the process descriptions are less detailed. Chapter 6 describes an advanced bipolar technology using oxide isolation. Chapter 7 illustrates an advanced NMOS process. Chapters 8, 9, 10, and 11 describe four advanced CMOS processes. The MOSIS and advanced twin-tub processes are presented in Chapter 8. A combined bipolar/CMOS process is discussed in Chapter 9. Chapter 10 describes the CMOS process applied in the fabrication of static random access memories. Chapter 11 briefly presents the basic concept of CMOS on sapphire.

The sources of information for this Atlas were many. Specific details about the processes presented in this book have been extracted from actual descriptions of IC manufacturing processes and the following references:

D. J. McGreivy and K. A. Pickar, Eds., *VLSI Technologies through the 80s and Beyond* (IEEE Computer Society Press: New York, 1982).

IEEE Journal of Solid-State Circuits, *Joint Special Issue on Very Large Scale of Integration* (February 1985, Volume SC-20).

Proceedings of *IEEE International Solid-State Circuit Conference*.

Proceedings of *IEEE International Electron Device Meeting*.

Several textbooks for the courses mentioned before were also used in the preparation of this text and are acknowledged on the appropriate pages. Thus, the process descriptions in this book are realistic, yet simplified. The reader who wishes to study VLSI processes in more detail should refer to the above list of references, to the additional references listed in the Appendix, and to the original process descriptions.

Finally, it is important to stress that all of the previously mentioned courses can benefit most from this book if students have their own copies of the Atlas. Independent study of the drawings and text will minimize valuable classroom time spent on this supplementary material. Our classroom experience also suggests that transparencies with enlarged drawings from the book are an invaluable teaching tool.[*] This is important because only precisely prepared drawings can speed up the explanations of VLSI processes to such an extent that they can be accommodated in the traditional courses.

Pittsburgh, Pennsylvania   W. Maly

---

[*] Macintosh disks with enlarged transparency versions of the drawings presented in the book can be obtained from the author.

Acknowledgments

There is a long list of individuals who contributed to this book in one way or another. Among them, I would like to mention the co-authors of four chapters: **David Greve, Jerzy Ruzyllo, Andrzej Strojwas, and Marek Syrzycki.** David Greve contributed to the text in Chapter 3. Jerzy Ruzyllo contributed to the text in Chapters 1 and 11. Andrzej Strojwas contributed to the text in Chapter 5. Marek Syrzycki contributed to the text in Chapter 4, and also provided very valuable help and a great deal of useful suggestions in the preparation of the camera ready version of this book.

Very valuable assistance was also provided by the editors from Benjamin/Cummings who encouraged me to write (i.e. to draw) this book. I am especially grateful to Martine H. Westermann and Craig S. Bartholomew for their help with English usage, and other issues which are very important to a newcomer to the American textbook market.

I would like to acknowledge the constructive contributions of the reviewers: T. V. Blalock, University of Tennessee; Bruce E. Deal, Fairchild Semiconductor Corporation; Lance A. Glasser, Massachusetts Institute of Technology; John R. Hauser, North Carolina State University; David A. Hodges, University of California, Berkeley; Hisham Z. Massoud, Duke University; Paul Van Halen, Portland State University; and Madhu Vora, Fairchild Semiconductor Corporation.

I would also like to express my appreciation to the people who provided me with the environment and information necessary to write this book. **Carnegie-Mellon University**, and in particular Steve Director, my Department Head, helped me a lot. Randall A. Hughes, Jerry Taylor, Bonnie Trifilo, and especially Dave Hanson, all from the **Fairchild Semiconductor Corporation**, helped me understand advanced processes. They also provided the SEM photographs presented in Chapter 10, which could not have been written without Fairchild's help.

I also would like to mention many people in Poland who at the early stages of my professional career "contaminated" my system-oriented mind with process-related doubts. Wieslaw Kuzmicz from the Technical University of Warsaw and Jan Koszur and Bozena Lesinska from the Scientific and Production Center of Semiconductors are among them. Wieslaw Kuzmicz is perhaps the most important indirect contributor to this book because he is a person with whom I spent thousands of hours discussing process-related issues in IC design.

Finally, I would like to say thank you to the two perhaps most important contributors -- my wife, Halina and my daughter, Kasia. They let me draw this book providing me with motivation. They also, many times, let me stay in my office, when they really needed me at home.

Table of Contents

Chapter 1
Processing Steps

with contributions from
Jerzy Ruzyllo

The fabrication process of an integrated circuit (IC) consists of a series of steps carried out in a specific order. These steps convert the circuit design into an operable silicon integrated circuit chip.

The way in which individual IC fabrication steps are carried out is of critical importance to the outcome of the manufacturing process. The main objective is to minimize the departure of geometrical features of the processed circuit from those determined during the design. To achieve this, a high degree of control over the parameters of each processing step is required. Equally rigid requirements apply to the physical and chemical properties of materials used for IC fabrication as well as to the cleanliness of the production environment.

The complexity of present integrated circuit devices calls for the use of a wide variety of processing techniques. The arsenal of equipment used includes specialized furnaces, plasma reactors, ion and electron beam machines, ultraviolet and X-ray sources, lasers, complex optical systems, and high vacuum systems.

The purpose of this chapter is to illustrate and explain processing steps that are used to create selected important features of the IC layout. The emphasis is placed on those steps which contribute most to the distortion of the device layout as compared to the design specifications.

1.1. Photolithography

Photolithography is a technique used in IC fabrication to transfer a desired pattern onto the surface of a silicon wafer. As such, photolithography is a key step in the entire circuit integration process. The basic concept of photolithography is illustrated in Fig. 1-1.

The starting point of the photolithographic process is a **mask** in which clear and opaque areas represent the pattern to be transferred onto the wafer (Fig. 1-1(a)). The mask consists of a thin film material, frequently chromium, deposited and photographically shaped on a high-quality glass plate which acts as a mechanical support for the mask. Pattern transfer by photolithography begins by coating the wafer with a thin film of photosensitive material referred to as **photoresist**. During wafer exposure with visible or ultraviolet (UV) light the mask prevents penetration of light through the opaque chromium while allowing radiation to pass through the clear glass (Fig. 1-1(b)). The chemical structure of photoresist is such that the UV light changes its solubility in a developing solution. The photoresist can then be locally removed from the surface of the wafer during a subsequent developing process. This exposes the underlying material, in this case silicon dioxide (SiO_2), to further processing in selected areas.

The geometry of the regions in which the photochemical reaction in the photoresist takes place corresponds to the pattern on the mask. The accuracy of the pattern transfer from the mask to the wafer determines the resolution of the photolithographic process. The higher the photolithographic resolution, the finer the geometrical features that can be patterned onto the wafer.

(a)

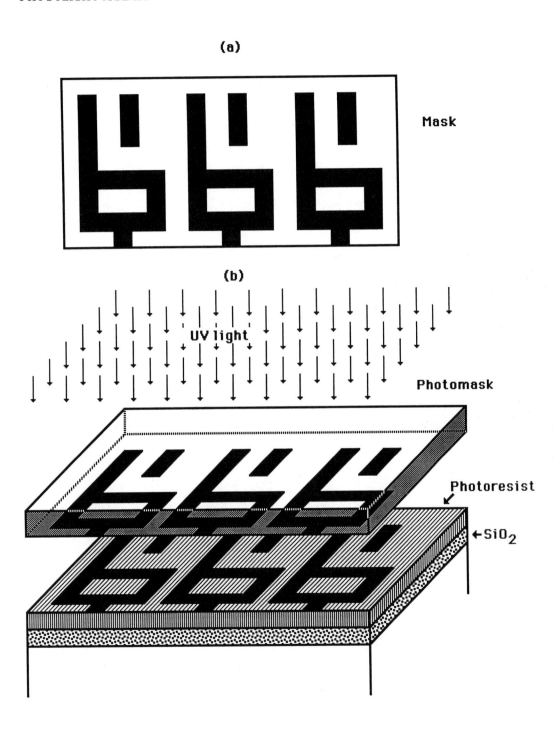

(b)

Figure 1-1: Photolithography - Basic concept.

1.1.1. Photolithography using a positive photoresist

Photoresist is a photosensitive polymer. The chemical structure of photoresist determines the result of its interaction with UV light during the photolithographic process described in the previous section. Photoresists are referred to as either **positive** or **negative.**

Fig. 1-2 illustrates the photolithographic process using positive photoresist that is exposed to UV light through the mask shown in Fig. 1-1 (a). As an example, patterning of a thin silicon dioxide layer is illustrated, but exactly the same procedure applies to the pattern transfer into any other material used in IC fabrication.

Positive photoresist is initially insoluble in the developing solution and becomes soluble after the exposure to UV radiation. Therefore, after the development photoresist remains on the wafer where the mask is opaque, while it is removed from the remaining areas (Fig. 1-2 (b)). The next step is removal of the uncovered oxide by etching. As a result, oxide remains on the surface only in the areas where it is protected by photoresist (Fig. 1-2 (b)). Finally, the photoresist is removed and the wafer is ready for subsequent processing steps. Note the resemblance of the dark contour on the mask (Fig. 1-1 (a)) to the final geometry of the oxide film (Fig. 1-2 (c)).

In general, positive photoresists are less sensitive (require longer exposure time) than negative photoresists, but they do provide better photolithographic resolution.

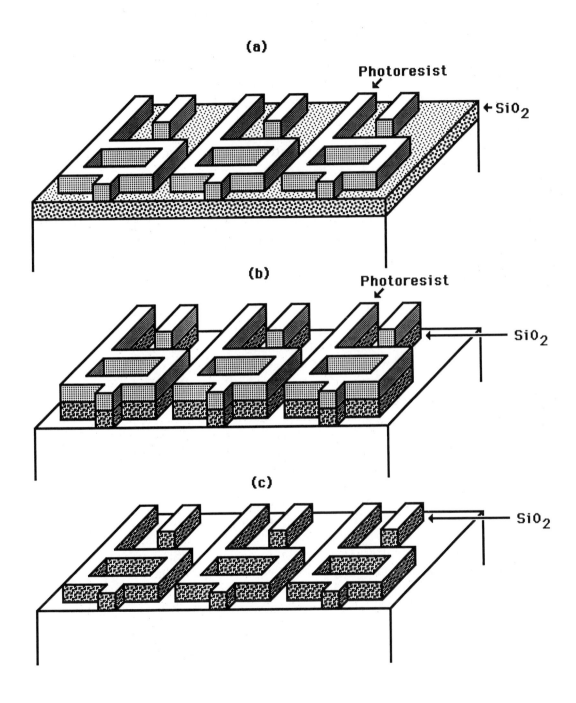

Figure 1-2: Photolithography using positive photoresist.

1.1.2. Photolithography using a negative photoresist

The photolithographic process using negative photoresist is similar to the process using positive resist discussed in the previous section. The only difference is that the negative photoresist is initially soluble in developer and becomes insoluble after exposure to UV light. The resist protected from the UV light by dark features on the mask remains soluble and is readily washed away during the developing process shown in Fig. 1-3 (a). The remaining steps in Fig. 1-3 (b) and (c) are exactly the same as in positive photolithography, but the final result is a reversal of the oxide pattern (see Fig. 1-2 (c)).

As stated before, negative resists are more sensitive than their positive counterparts. Due to their inferior resolution, however, they are less commonly used in the manufacturing of high-density integrated circuits.

1.1.3. Other lithography techniques

Photolithography uses UV light to expose the resist. The resolution of this technique is limited by diffraction at the edges of opaque areas in the mask (see Fig. 1-1). Diffraction becomes significant only when the size of the pattern becomes comparable to a wavelength of the illuminating radiation. Present integrated circuits use minimum dimensions near 1 μm (10^{-6} m), while the UV radiation used for photoresist exposure has a wavelength of about 0.3 - 0.4 μm. Further reduction in the minimum dimensions will therefore require the use of sources with shorter wavelengths. A lithography technique using X-rays for the resist exposure is referred to as **X-ray lithography**, and requires the use of different lithography masks and resists. An alternative solution is offered by applying an electron beam (E-beam) to expose the resist. Since the E-beam can be very finely focused, **E-beam lithography** is capable of writing the pattern directly into the electron sensitive resist by scanning the E-beam according to the desired pattern. No mask is needed using this technique of resist exposure, and a very high accuracy of pattern delineation is achieved. Similar results can be obtained using an ion beam instead of an electron beam. Ion beam lithography offers several advantages, but the sensitivity of the resist used in this type of exposure still needs to be improved. Unfortunately, both E-beam and ion beam techniques are very slow and therefore very expensive.

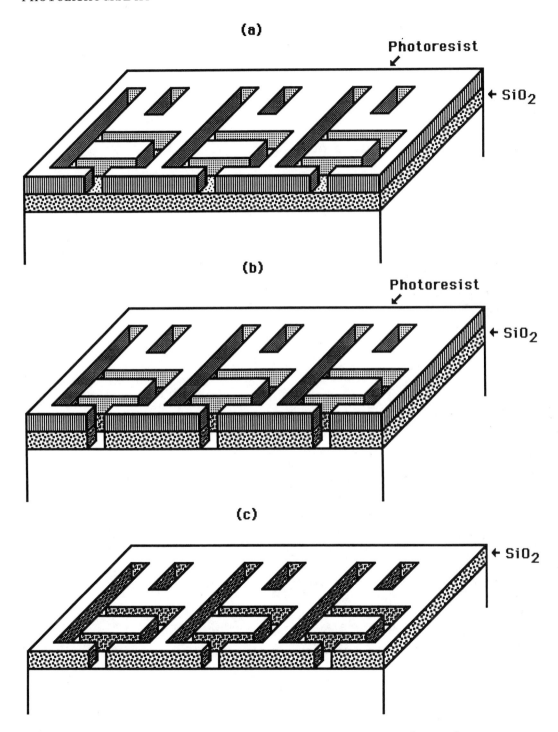

Figure 1-3: Photolithography using negative photoresist.

1.2. Oxidation

Thermal oxidation is a process in which silicon (Si) reacts with oxygen to form a continuous layer of high-quality silicon dioxide (SiO_2). A film of the same composition but of lower quality can be formed in other ways.

1.2.1. Thermal oxidation of silicon

Thermal oxidation of silicon, which results in the formation of a thin film of silicon dioxide, is one of the most frequently used steps in the course of IC processing. In silicon IC technology the thermal SiO_2 layer is used as:

1. a mask during dopant diffusion,

2. a junction passivation,

3. an insulating field oxide, and

4. a gate dielectric in MOS devices.

Thermal oxidation is performed by exposing silicon to an ambient containing oxygen or water vapor at an elevated temperature ($900\,°C$ to $1100\,°C$). The oxidation rate is significantly faster when the ambient contains water vapor; this process is referred to as a **wet** oxidation. Fig. 1-4 illustrates the thermal oxidation process.

Oxidation begins as soon as the silicon surface is exposed to the oxidizing ambient at an elevated temperature (Fig. 1-4 (a)). Two processes are involved during oxidation: first, diffusion of the oxidant through the silicon dioxide film to the silicon-silicon dioxide interface; and second, a chemical reaction with the silicon surface to form silicon dioxide. Initially, the oxidation rate is controlled by the rate of the chemical reaction of silicon with the oxidant (Fig. 1-4 (b)). As the oxide grows thicker, the rate of oxidation is limited by the diffusion of oxidant through the silicon dioxide film.

Note that part of the silicon substrate is consumed during oxidation. The thickness of the substrate consumed is approximately 44% of the final oxide thickness.

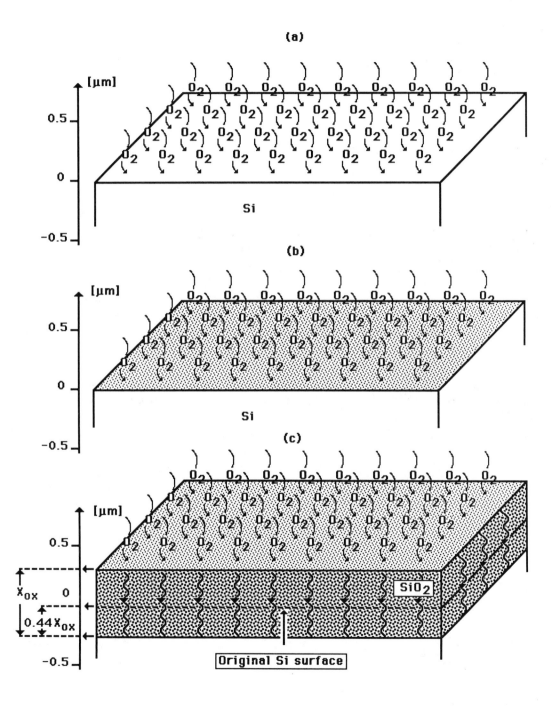

Figure 1-4: Oxidation of the silicon surface.

1.2.2. Oxidation through a window in the oxide

In a situation frequently encountered in IC fabrication, the oxide grows on silicon that is partially covered by oxide from previous steps. Due to the mechanism of thermal oxidation, the oxidation rate of bare silicon is higher than that in the areas covered with oxide. Therefore, the process leaves a characteristic mark on the silicon surface in the form of a **recess** in the window area. This is illustrated in Fig. 1-5.

According to the discussion in Section 1.2.1, oxidation initially occurs at a much faster rate in the window than in the surrounding areas (Fig. 1-5 (a)). Oxide growth in the window is accompanied by the consumption of silicon in the growing oxide (Fig. 1-5 (b)). As the oxidation continues, the oxidation rate and consequently the rate of silicon consumption become more uniform over the entire area of the wafer (Fig. 1-5 (c)). Due to the initially differing oxidation rates, a recess always remains in the underlying silicon (Fig. 1-5 (c)). An important consequence of the described process is that the recess in the silicon substrate remains after the oxide is removed from the surface (Fig. 1-5 (d)). This indentation indicates the edges of regions which have been created by using an oxide mask. Such edges are used to align masks for subsequent processing steps.

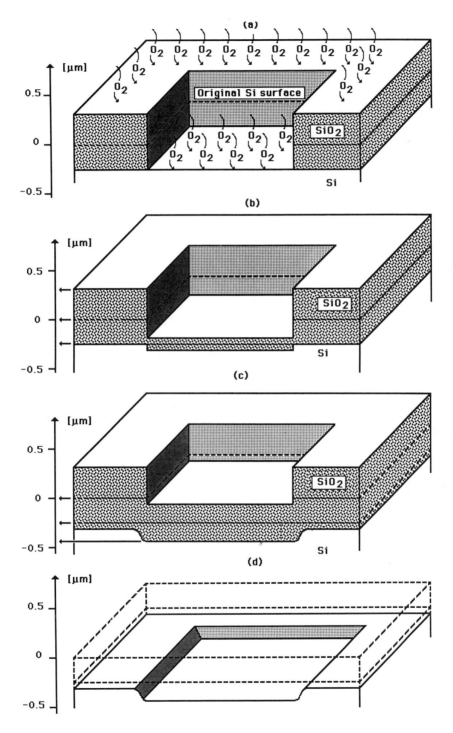

Figure 1-5: Oxidation through a window in the oxide.

1.2.3. Selective oxide growth

Local oxidation is a common isolation technique in NMOS, CMOS, and bipolar technology.

In order to perform localized oxidation, a masking material is required over areas of Si substrate where growth of an oxide is not desired. Silicon nitride (Si_3N_4) can effectively block oxidizing species $(O_2$ or $H_2O)$ and, at the same time, is resistant to the high temperature required for oxidation. Fig. 1-6 shows selective oxide growth on silicon.

The first step in local oxidation is deposition and patterning of a Si_3N_4 film of appropriate thickness (Fig. 1-6 (a)). Once the oxidation mask is thus defined, the wafer is subjected to the thermal oxidation process. Usually, wet oxidation is used as an oxidizing ambient to grow an oxide thick enough to allow significant penetration of silicon (see Fig. 1-4). Since oxidation of silicon proceeds not only in the direction normal to the surface, but also laterally into the pad oxide, the result is penetration of the growing oxide beneath the nitride mask (Fig. 1-6 (b)). Simultaneous volume expansion of the growing oxide takes place, and hence the edges of the Si_3N_4 mask are lifted up. As oxidation progresses, both effects become more prominent (Fig. 1-6 (c)).

An undesired result of local oxidation is the formation of a specific geometrical feature referred to as a **bird's beak**. The bird's beak causes the active area of the device to be significantly smaller than the size of the initial nitride mask (Fig. 1-6 (d)). The initial dimensions of the nitride mask can be corrected to compensate for this error.

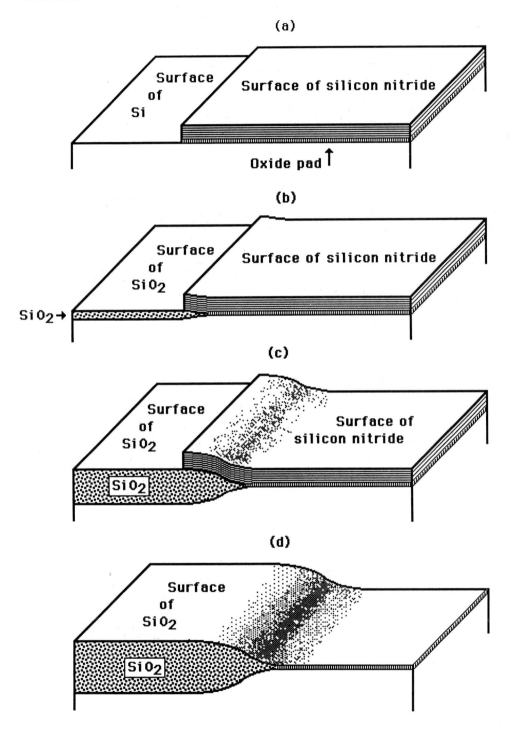

Figure 1-6: Selective SiO$_2$ growth, using local oxidation.

1.3. Layer deposition

Thin layers of both conducting substances (metals, metal silicides, or low-resistivity polycrystalline silicon) and insulating materials (silicon dioxide, silicon nitride, and phosphosilicate glass) constitute an important part of any semiconductor device. This section illustrates methods for **thin film deposition**.

1.3.1. Deposition - general nature of the process

In contrast to the growth of the silicon dioxide layer by thermal oxidation (refer to Section 1.2.1), deposition processes do not involve a chemical reaction with the substrate. In deposition, all components of the growing layer are supplied from external sources, and the chemical composition of the layer is independent of the composition of the substrate (Fig. 1-7 (a)). Deposition of the thin solid layer in this manner does not cause consumption of the silicon substrate (Fig. 1-7 (b)) as is the case in thermal oxidation of silicon (see Fig. 1-4).

Deposition processes are usually carried out in a vapor phase under reduced pressure or in a vacuum. An exception to this rule is the application of photoresist by a spin-on technique, in which photoresist is deposited in liquid form and then thermally solidified.

The configuration of the deposited thin layer reflects the topography of the substrate (Fig. 1-7 (c)). This is an important consideration since in the case of high steps patterned on the substrate, coverage of the steps by the deposited material may not be conformal. The resulting nonuniformity of thickness of the deposited layer can cause reliability problems in the final device (note the area indicated by the arrow). Nonuniform thickness of a metal layer, caused by the above phenomena, may result in a nonuniform distribution of the current density along the conducting line. High current density in the thinner spots (see arrow in Fig. 1-7 (c)) can cause a current-induced metal migration and thus a metal connection break.

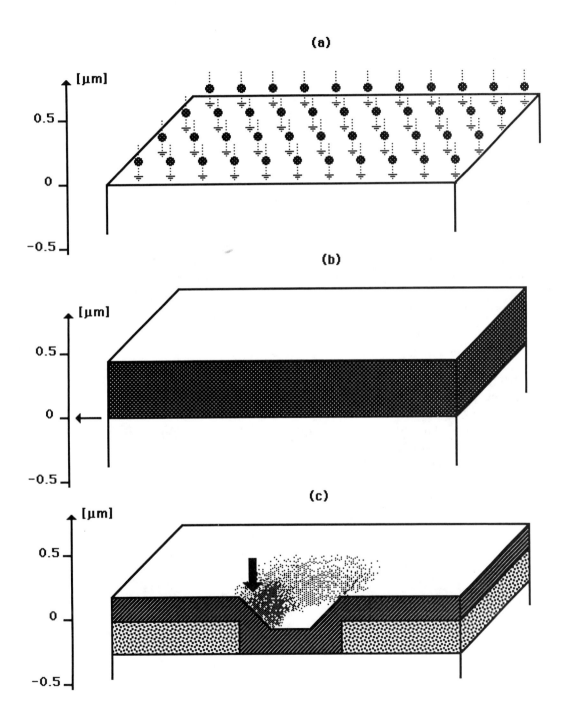

Figure 1-7: Deposition of the thin solid layer.

1.3.2. Crystal structure of the deposited layer

From the point of view of atomic structure, solids can be either **crystalline** or **amorphous**. The former are characterized by a long-range order of atoms, while a short-range order is characteristic of the latter. Crystalline materials can either be **single crystal**, where the long-range order is maintained throughout the entire solid, or **polycrystalline**, where the long-range order is maintained only within randomly oriented grains.

Only single-crystal silicon is used to fabricate wafers in IC manufacturing. However, layers deposited on wafers can take any of the forms described above. Fig. 1-8 illustrates structures consisting of single-crystal (a), polycrystalline (b), and amorphous (c) material deposited on the single-crystal silicon substrate.

In the case of deposition of a single-crystal layer on single-crystal substrate (Fig. 1-8(a)), the crystal structure of the substrate is exactly reproduced in the deposited layer. This type of material deposition is referred to as **epitaxy**, and is considered in Section 1.3.4. In the other two cases shown in Fig. 1-8 the structure of the layer is independent of the crystal structure of the substrate.

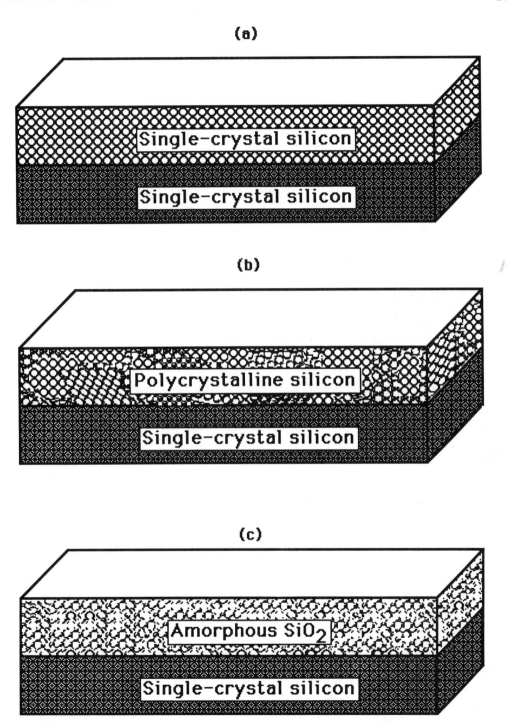

Figure 1-8:   Thin layer of materials in three different crystallographic
forms deposited on single-crystal silicon.

1.3.3. PVD and CVD processes

As mentioned before, most of the layer deposition processes are carried out in the vapor phase. If the material to be deposited does not react chemically during deposition, then the process is referred to as **Physical Vapor Deposition** or **PVD** (Fig. 1-9 (a)). An example of such a process is the deposition of aluminum by vacuum evaporation or sputtering. If, on the other hand, the deposited material is a product of a chemical reaction in the vapor phase on the surface of the substrate or in its vicinity, then the process is termed **Chemical Vapor Deposition** or **CVD** (Fig. 1-9 (b)).

Vapor deposition processes are very common in IC manufacturing. They allow deposition of a wide variety of materials in the form of thin layers. Typical IC technology uses:

1. The CVD technique to deposit silicon dioxide (SiO_2), silicon nitride (Si_3N_4), and both single-crystal and polycrystalline silicon.

2. The PVD technique to deposit metals, primarily aluminum.

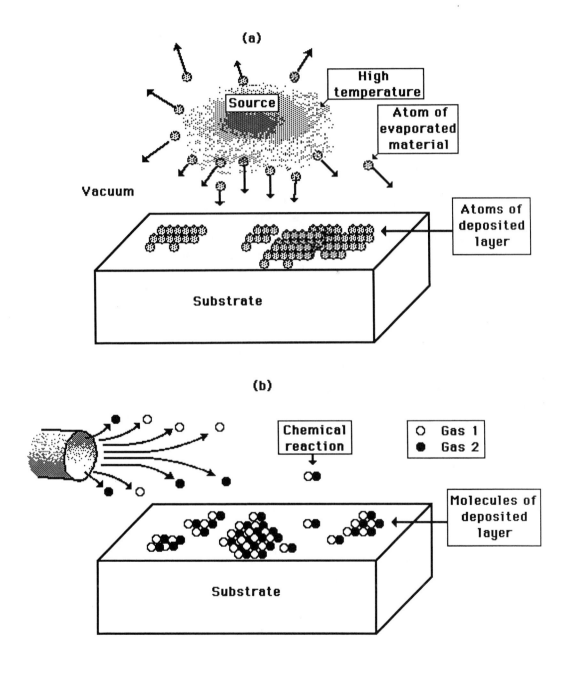

Figure 1-9: Vapor deposition. PVD (a) and CVD (b).

1.3.4. Epitaxy

A special case of the CVD process is deposition of a single-crystal silicon layer on a single-crystal silicon substrate. **Epitaxial layers** are used in both MOS and bipolar technologies as discussed in later chapters. Fig. 1-10 stresses the unique nature of epitaxy in that the crystal structure of the growing film is a continuation of the crystal structure of the substrate (Fig. 1-10 (a)). The **doping type and level** in the epi layer can be easily controlled, and therefore epitaxy can be used to create a sandwich of differently doped layers with the same crystalline structure. The concentration of impurities in each epi layer can be kept uniform.

Due to the nature of the growth process any feature on the surface of the substrate is transferred to the surface of the epi layer (Fig. 1-10 (a)). Thus edges of the recess patterned on the surface of the substrate by, for example, the oxidation described in Section 1.2 can be seen on the surface of the IC after the epi layer deposition (Fig. 1-10 (b)). The surface cleanliness of the silicon substrate is especially important before epitaxy. Epitaxial deposition is prone to defects and contamination. Surface defects nucleate defects such as stacking faults in the growing epi layer (Fig. 1-10 (c)). Defects in the epi layer can substantially degrade the performance of devices fabricated in it.

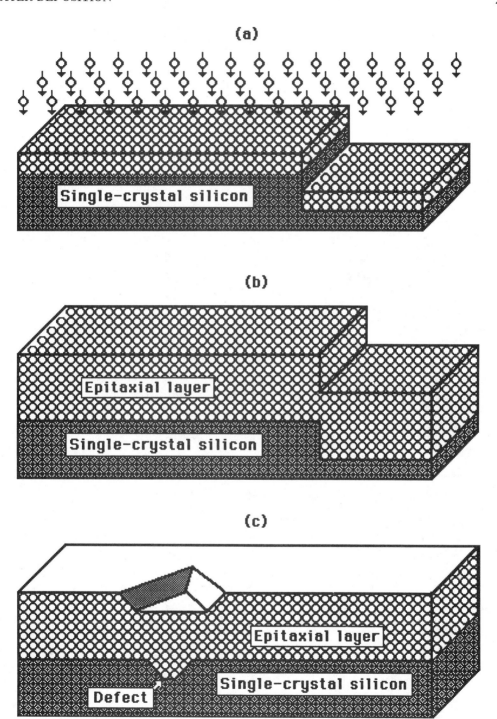

Figure 1-10: Epitaxy and mechanisms of
defect formation in the epitaxial layer.

1.4. Etching

The process that immediately follows the photolithographic step discussed in Section 1.1 is the removal of material from areas of the wafer unprotected by photoresist. Various **etching** techniques are used for this purpose. Etching processes are characterized by their **selectivity** (for example, the etching agent should attack SiO_2, but not photoresist and silicon) and their degree of **anisotropy**. Anisotropic etching occurs in one direction only, in contrast to the undesired isotropic etching, in which material is removed at the same rate in all directions.

The etching processes used in IC fabrication can take place either in a liquid or gas phase. They can be purely chemical (material is removed by dissolution which is inherently a highly selective but isotropic process), purely physical (material is removed by bombardment with high-energy ions, which is inherently an anisotropic but unselective process), or a combination of both (material is removed by bombardment with reactive ions that also react chemically with the etched material). In the last case, a compromise between selectivity and anisotropy of etching can be obtained.

1.4.1. Wet etching

The **wet etching** technique is performed by exposing the wafer to liquid chemicals. As such, it is an isotropic process which results in lateral deformation of the etched pattern. Fig. 1-11 illustrates this effect throughout various stages of the wet etching process (Fig. 1-11 (a), (b) and (c)). Upon completion of etching and the removal of photoresist, a pattern is revealed that significantly departs from the desired pattern (Fig. 1-11 (d)).

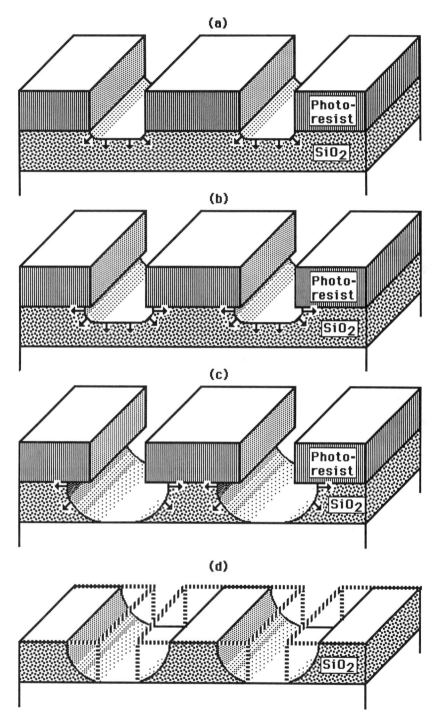

Figure 1-11: Wet etching.

1.4.2. Dry etching

Etching carried out in a gas under reduced pressure is referred to as **dry etching**. Dry etching can combine the advantages of chemical and physical etching, so it can be simultaneously anisotropic and selective.

In Fig. 1-12 (a) and (b), various stages of the dry etching process are shown. After the etching is completed (Fig. 1-12 (c)), and photoresists are removed, a pattern is revealed that accurately reproduces the pattern previously defined in the resist (Fig. 1-12 (d)). Dry etching processes must be used in fabrication of fine-geometry devices where lateral deformations of the IC layout are unacceptable.

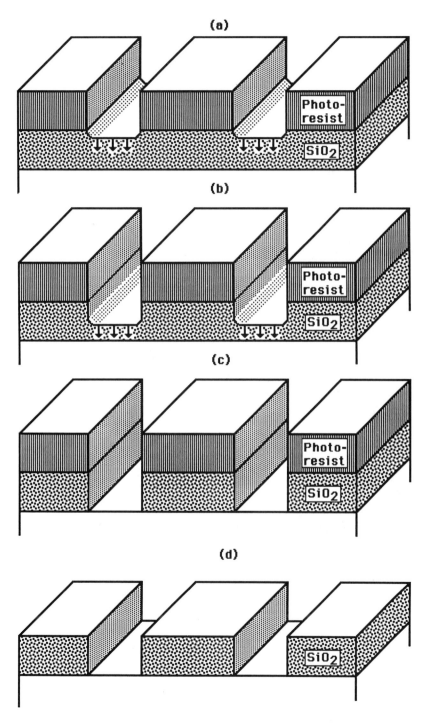

Figure 1-12: Dry etching.

1.5. Diffusion

Solid state diffusion is a process which allows atoms to move within a solid at elevated temperatures. Diffusion takes place only when atoms are nonuniformly distributed in the solid, i.e. a concentration gradient must exist. Under these conditions (elevated temperature and a concentration gradient) atoms will move by diffusion in the direction of decreasing concentration.

Diffusion is commonly used in IC technology to introduce dopants into the semiconductor substrate. Dopants affect the conductivity or change the type of conductivity (from n to p or vice versa) of selected regions within the substrate.

1.5.1. Dopant diffusion in silicon

Common **dopants** used in silicon device manufacturing are boron (B) to create p-type regions, and phosphorus (P), arsenic (As), and antimony (Sb) to create n-type regions. All of them substitute for silicon in the silicon lattice and diffuse by jumping from one lattice site to another. Fig. 1-13 schematically represents such a process.

Consider the large concentration of dopant atoms in contact with an area on the silicon surface (Fig. 1-13(a)). When the temperature is high enough (usually from $900\,^\circ$C to $1100\,^\circ$C), the dopant atoms move by diffusion into the silicon. The dopants will spread out in the silicon both vertically and laterally as indicated in Fig. 1-13. The rate of dopant motion by diffusion in silicon at the given temperature is different for each type of dopant, and is characterized by a **diffusion coefficient**. The process of diffusion will slow as soon as the temperature of the wafer is reduced significantly below the temperature of diffusion, and it essentially stops altogether below about $700\,^\circ$C. The shaded area in Fig. 1-13(b) is the region of different substrate conductivity which results from the introduction of dopants into the silicon.

Note that the distribution of dopants within the diffused region is inherently nonuniform, i.e. it decreases gradually with distance from the dopant source at the surface.

(a)

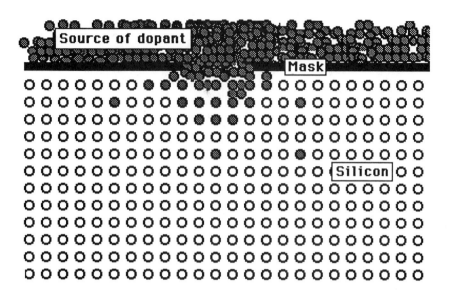

(b)

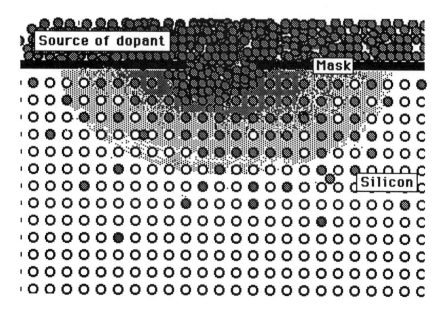

Figure 1-13: Diffusion mechanisms.

1.5.2. Diffusion techniques

In the practical applications of diffusion in IC manufacturing, the key issue is to localize dopant introduction in selected regions of the silicon. For this purpose, the silicon dioxide is used to act as a barrier, or mask, against dopant diffusion. The film of SiO_2 is grown on silicon by thermal oxidation (see Section 1.2.1). Then it is patterned by photolithography (see Section 1.1) in such a way that the oxide is removed from the silicon surface only in the areas in which diffusion of dopants into the silicon substrate is desired.

Through openings (windows) in the oxide, dopant atoms have undisrupted access to the silicon substrate. In the remaining areas that are protected by the oxide, dopants first have to diffuse through the oxide before they will reach silicon. By taking advantage of the low diffusion coefficient in SiO_2 of the dopants listed in Section 1.5.1, and by maintaining an adequately thick masking oxide, the diffusion into the oxide-protected areas of silicon is effectively prevented. Because of the need to form masking oxides, all diffusion steps in IC fabrication are preceded by thermal oxidation.

Fig. 1-14(a) shows the outcome of the dopant diffusion into silicon through the window in the masking oxide. Note that due to the lateral diffusion (see Fig. 1-13(a)), the actual size of the diffused region is larger than the window in the masking oxide. It is imperative to take this effect into account in the course of designing the IC layout. Fig. 1-14(a) also depicts the layer of material containing a large quantity of dopant atoms that acts as a dopant source. Its nature is discussed in the next section.

The diffusion process results in a dopant distribution in silicon as shown in Fig. 1-14(b). Consider the diffusion of n-type dopant into p-type silicon substrate. In such a process, the p-n junction occurs in the plane in which the concentration C of the diffused n-type dopants decreases to the value that is equal to the concentration C_{sub} of p-type dopants in the substrate. The junction depth x_j can be precisely controlled by selecting the appropriate temperature and time of diffusion.

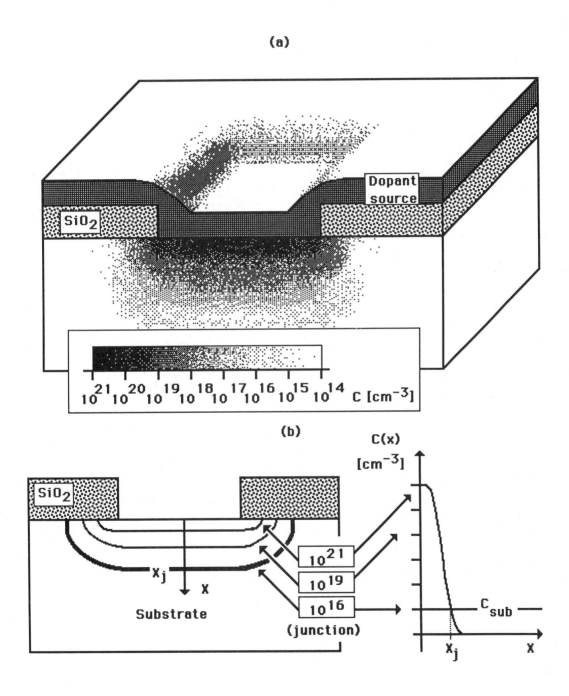

Figure 1-14:   Diffusion of dopants through a window in the SiO$_2$ layer.

1.5.3. Constant source diffusion

The way in which diffusion processes in microcircuit fabrication are carried out depends on the design of the given feature of the device layout. If a high dopant concentration at the silicon surface and a relatively shallow junction are required, then the single-step **constant source diffusion** is sufficient to meet the objectives of the dopant introduction process.

The constant source diffusion takes place when a wafer is exposed to a dopant source of constant concentration during the entire diffusion period. In practice, the dopant source is a thin solid film of a mixture of dopant oxide (e.g. P_2O_5 or B_2O_3) and silicon dioxide formed on the wafer surface (see Fig. 1-14(a)). The number of dopant atoms in such a material is high enough for the source not to be depleted in the course of diffusion, and hence the term constant (unlimited) source dopant atoms.

The various stages of constant source diffusion are shown in Fig. 1-15 (a). Right after the source is brought into contact with the silicon surface (t=0), dopant atoms start to move into the silicon, and as time goes on more dopants are transferred to the substrate. These atoms are gradually diffusing deeper into the silicon, but their concentration at the surface (C_s) remains constant. This process is illustrated by the variations of dopant profiles with time of constant source diffusion in Fig. 1-15(b). Note that the temperature and time of constant source diffusion determine the number of dopants that are transferred from the source to the silicon.

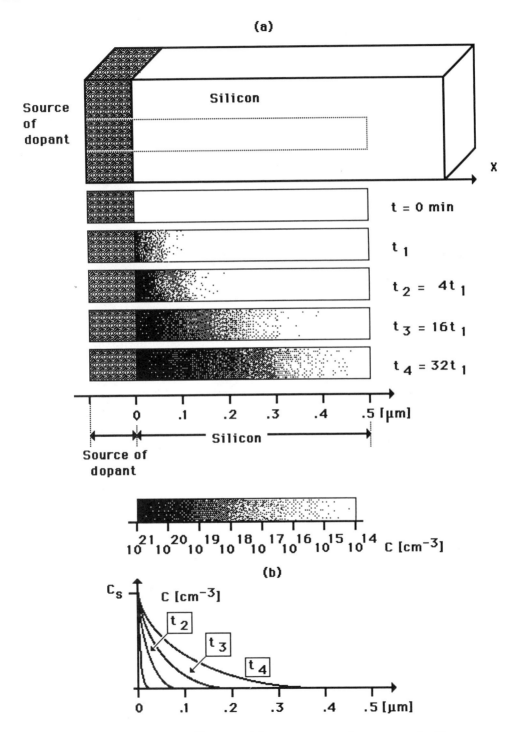

Figure 1-15: Diffusion with constant surface concentration.

1.5.4. Two-step diffusion

As mentioned earlier, whenever a high surface concentration C_s of dopants and shallow p-n junctions are required, a one-step constant source diffusion may be sufficient to meet the requirements of the device layout. Very often, however, it is essential to reduce the surface concentration of dopants and/or to drive the junction deeper into the silicon substrate. For this purpose an additional high-temperature step referred to as **drive-in** is needed. In this way, a **two-step diffusion process** is developed in which the first step is a constant source diffusion as discussed in the previous section. This step, commonly referred to as a **predeposition**, is then followed by the drive-in. The basic feature of the drive-in process is that no additional dopant atoms are introduced into the wafer, so only those incorporated into the silicon during the predeposition step are actually undergoing redistribution.

Fig. 1-16(a) illustrates the concept of two-step diffusion. After a time t_2 of predeposition, the dopants are reaching a very high concentration at the surface of the substrate and at the same time are distributed only within the very shallow region underneath it. To achieve the goals of the drive-in process, the dopant source has to be separated from the silicon surface so that after the predeposition no more dopants are allowed to penetrate to the substrate. One method to meet this requirement is to etch the material acting as a dopant source from the surface of the wafer. A second method, illustrated in Fig. 1-16(a), relies on the separation of the dopant source from the silicon by growing an oxide layer between them (See Section 1.2). In such a case, only dopants introduced during predeposition will undergo redistribution, i.e. will move both laterally and vertically with respect to the surface. Fig. 1-16(b) shows the dopant profile during (time t_1) and after the predeposition (time t_2). Fig. 1-16(c) illustrates the corresponding variations of the dopant profile during the drive-in step. Note the decrease of surface concentration, and increase of junction depth with time.

It is very important to recognize that once dopants are introduced into silicon, any subsequent high-temperature processing step (e.g. oxidation) can cause an unintentional redistribution of dopants. In the fine-geometry ICs such variations of the dopant profile are unacceptable. This consideration restricts the use of lengthy high-temperature processes in such cases, and calls for either reduction of process temperatures, or very brief exposure of the processed wafer to high temperatures.

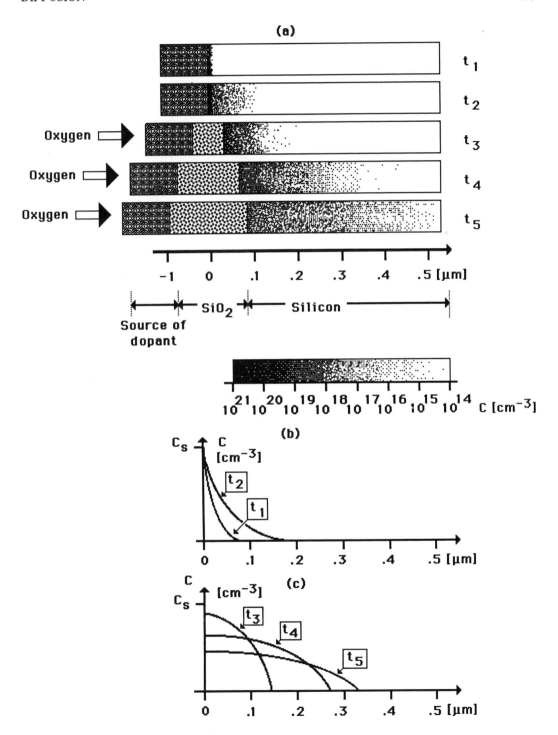

Figure 1-16: Two step diffusion process.

1.6. Implantation

The alternative to the diffusion technique of dopant introduction used in IC manufacturing is **ion implantation**. From the processing point of view, the main difference between these two techniques results from the significantly lower process temperature in the ion implantation. This advantage combined with a much decreased lateral spreading of the doped region as well as overall better control over the dopant profile during ion implantation have led to the preferential use of this technique in high-density microcircuit fabrication. On the other hand, diffusion remains a dominant doping technique in the numerous applications where precision of the dopant profile is of less critical importance.

1.6.1. Nature of the implantation process

In an ion implanter, the electrically neutral dopant atoms in the gas phase are first converted into ions. Then, a collimated ion beam is formed in which ions are accelerated to gain high kinetic energy. These high-energy ions are directed toward the silicon wafer. Ions bombarding the surface have enough energy to enter the silicon, where they gradually lose their energy due to collisions with atoms in the substrate. Eventually, the ions come to rest after covering a certain distance from the surface referred to as a range. As a result, the highest concentration of implanted dopants is obtained not at the surface, as was the case in the diffusion process, but deeper in the substrate (Fig. 1-17). The number of collisions of the ions with substrate atoms and the energy lost per collision are random variables. Therefore, the implanted ions are spatially distributed in the substrate as shown in Fig. 1-17(b).

Since the entire wafer is subjected to ion bombardment during the ion implantation process, selected areas of surfaces have to be protected (masked) to achieve local doping. A convenient feature of ion implantation is that essentially any thin film material applied in the silicon IC fabrication, for example SiO_2 (Fig. 1-17(a)), photoresist, Si_3N_4, poly Si, or metal, can be used for this purpose provided it is sufficiently thick.

One important shortcoming of the ion implantation process is damage that occurs in the crystal lattice of single-crystal silicon substrate as a result of bombardment by high-energy ions. This damage causes unacceptable degradation of silicon properties, and thus a restoration of the crystallographic order within the substrate is needed. To achieve this, after ion implantation the wafer has to be annealed at an appropriate temperature and for an appropriate period of time.

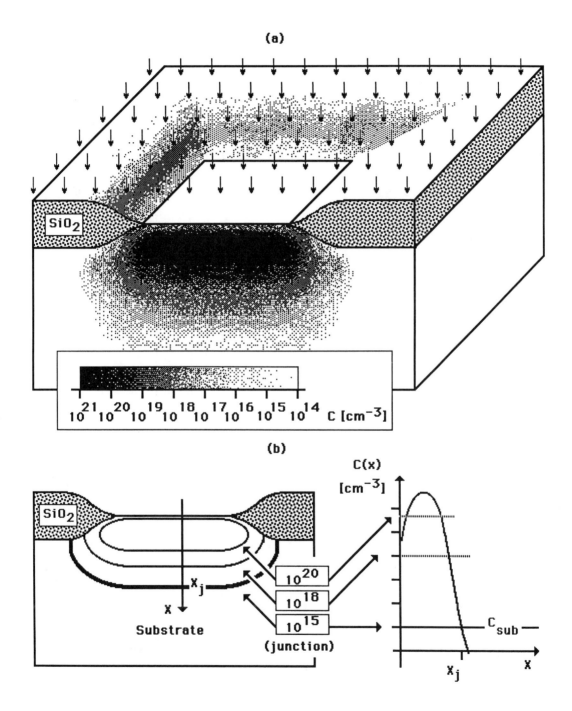

Figure 1-17: Ion implantation of dopants through a window
in an SiO_2 layer.

1.6.2. Variables of the implantation process

Fig. 1-18 schematically illustrates the relationship between parameters of the ion implantation process and the dopant profile. In Fig. 1-18(a) the beam of incident dopant ions is shown bombarding the silicon surface. The two important parameters of ion implantation are **dose**, expressed in number of ions per cm^2, and **energy**, in eV, of ions in the incident beam. The former determines the concentration of dopants introduced into the semiconductor, while the latter determines the range of ion penetration within the substrate, i.e. the junction depth. The variations of dopant distribution depending on the dose and energy are shown in Fig. 1-18(b).

Once implanted in the silicon, the dopant atoms behave in exactly the same way as those introduced by diffusion. This means that they will undergo redistribution under any high-temperature treatment given to the wafer (refer to Section 1.5.4). Fig. 1-18(c) shows results of redistribution during time t_1 of dopants implanted at the same dose, but at different energy levels. Fig. 1-18(d) and (e) show the profiles of implanted dopants right after the implantation and after redistribution, respectively.

The post-implantation thermal treatment that can potentially cause dopant redistribution cannot be eliminated from the processing sequence. This is because, as was stated earlier, annealing is required to remove damage created in the crystal lattice by the ion implantation process. At the same time, it serves to activate those dopant atoms that remain electrically neutral after the implantation, and thus are not contributing to the desired changes of the semiconductor conductivity. In high-complexity and very fine- geometry microcircuits any dopant redistribution can significantly alter the dimensions of the device. Therefore, the post-implantation annealing in such cases has to be carried out with elaborate wafer heating techniques which will allow achievement of the goals of annealing without causing dopant redistribution. In these techniques exposure times of implanted regions to high temperatures are very brief.

It is worth noting that, provided the energy of incident ions is sufficiently high, the dopants can be implanted in silicon through a thin film of material, such as SiO_2, that is covering its surface. It is clear that in such cases the film has to be thinner than the minimum thickness required for the oxide to act as a mask during the implantation. This aspect of the ion implantation technique is finding numerous practical applications in IC manufacturing.

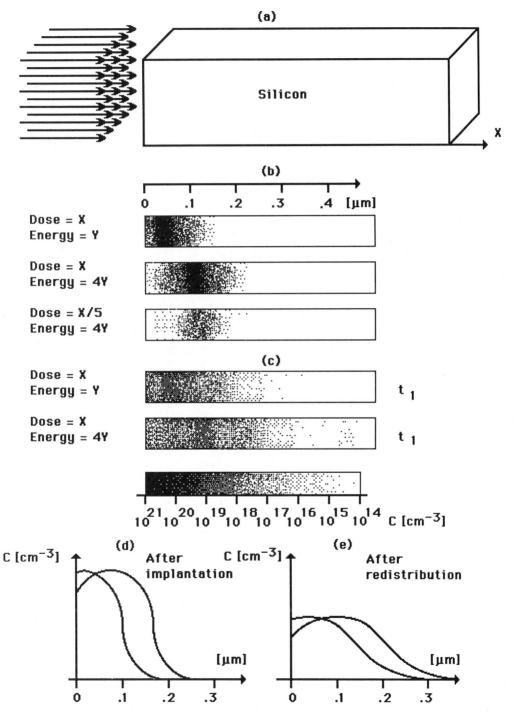

Figure 1-18: Effect of process variables in ion implantation.

Chapter 2
The Process-Design Relationship

An IC is created by performing a design and then executing the manufacturing process. The manufacturing process is organized as a sequence of processing steps executed according to the description of the process referred to as a **technology**. The technology also provides basic information used in the IC design. This chapter presents some elements of the relationships between design, manufacturing process, and technology in order to explain some of the design characteristics that have an origin in the process realities.

The relationship that will be emphasized in this chapter shows some of the differences between the actual manufacturing process and an "idealized" concept of the process that is used in the design. These differences have to be clearly seen and understood, because they determine key elements of the design methodology. Thus, they decide and explain basic features of the drawings and photographs presented in this book.

2.1. From the layout design to IC fabrication

Before a discussion of the main topic of this chapter we must present some basic facts about both design and the manufacturing process in this section.

2.1.1. IC design

IC design is a very complex process that involves hundreds of decisions dealing with the variety of IC performances and manufacturing-related issues. The final phase in the design is the creation of an **IC layout**; i.e. the creation of the drawing representing the geometry of the designed circuit. For a given process such a drawing uniquely defines the IC geometry and therefore the performance of the designed circuit.

The layout of an IC is defined as a set of polygons that determines the presence or absence of regions in a number of conducting and isolating layers. In other words, an IC layout shows from which part of the IC surface such materials as metal, silicon dioxide, photoresist, and so on should be removed, and where other materials should be deposited.

An IC layout can be created using several techniques. The most popular one is illustrated in Fig. 2-1. In this method a layout is created by assembling a drawing of the device using polygons representing different IC layers. In a typical case such a drawing is created using graphic terminals with different colors representing different layers of the IC to be produced (in Fig. 2-1 colors are represented by different shadings).

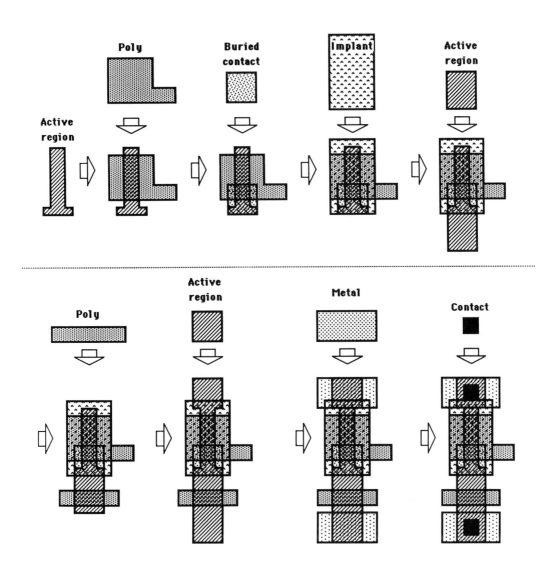

Figure 2-1: An example of a sequence of manipulations which
may be applied to create a layout of an NMOS inverter.

2.1.2. Photolithographic masks

During the design the IC layout is represented by a set of numbers that can be manipulated to create a composite drawing of IC masks on the screen of the terminal or on the color plotter. In the manufacturing process a "hard copy" of this layout is needed in the form of photolithographic masks.

Typically, the IC design is transformed into a set of masks in a sequence of steps illustrated in Fig. 2-2. First, coordinates of all elements of the IC composite drawing are computed (taking into account all necessary resizing operations that are supposed to compensate for various systematic errors anticipated in the process). Then data representing different layers are separated (Fig. 2-2 (c) and (d)) and an image of each IC layer is produced. Typically, such images are engraved on the surface of glass plates covered with chromium, using a photographic technique and pattern generator or E-beam equipment. Masks created in this way are called **master masks**.

Next master masks are scaled down (Fig. 2-2 (e-f)) and duplicated (Fig. 2-2 (g-h)) so that **working masks** made in this way contain a couple of tens to a couple of hundreds of the same images as the master masks. The size of the working mask is such that with a single exposure the entire area of a single manufacturing wafer can be covered.

In the newer lithography techniques, working masks are not needed and the image from the master mask is transferred directly onto the surface of the wafer (the master mask is then called a **reticle**). Special high-precision optical step-and-repeat cameras are used for this purpose.

Data that describe a single IC layer can also be used to project an image directly onto the surface of the manufacturing wafer using an electron beam (**EB**) technique. In this technique a deflected beam of electrons exposes appropriate regions directly on the surface of the photoresist.

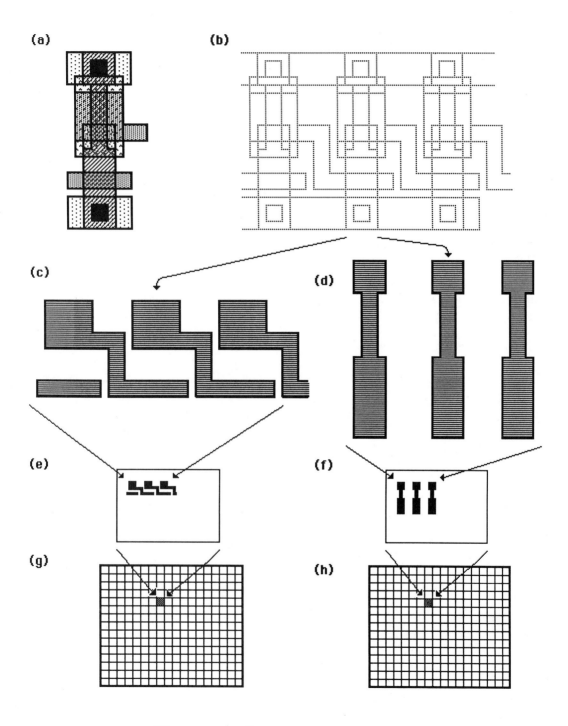

Figure 2-2: Design-mask transformation.

2.1.3. The IC manufacturing process

The manufacturing process is performed on **wafers** which are thin slices of semiconductor cylindrical ingot (See Fig. 2-3). The diameters of manufacturing wafers are such that a single wafer can accommodate a couple of tens to several hundreds of IC's. Typically, all IC's created on a single wafer have the same geometry. Exceptions are test structures that are fabricated in a couple (5 to 7) of sites on the wafer. Such test structures are used to monitor the quality of the process.

Each manufacturing wafer passes hundreds of processing steps. Some of these steps can be performed on a single wafer at a time, some on several wafers. A set of wafers processed simultaneously is called a **lot**.

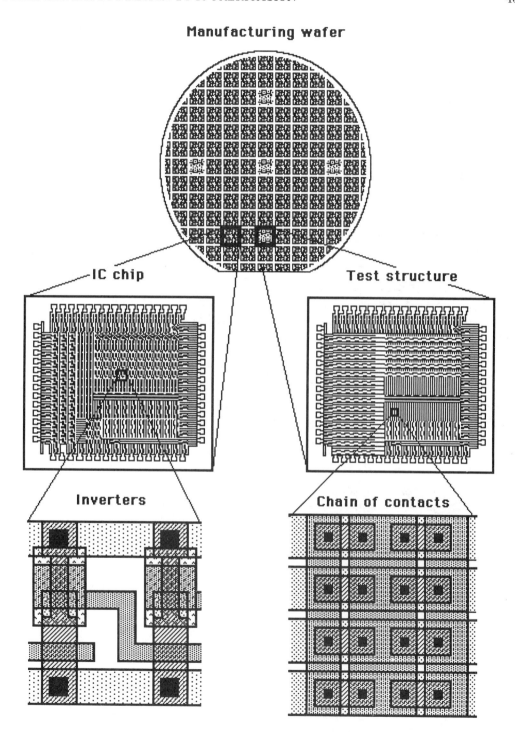

Figure 2-3: Manufacturing wafer.

At each manufacturing step, wafers are affected by process conditions that are determined by both **process control** and **random process disturbances** (Fig. 2-4). Progress of the process is evaluated after each major processing step. When manufacturing errors or abnormal disturbances are detected, wafers affected by such disturbances are discarded.

The problem is that during the process only major process abnormalities can be detected. Thus, at the end of the process (Fig. 2-4) all fabricated IC's have to be tested to detect circuits that do not meet expected specifications.

Note that due to the random disturbances inherent in the process, each manufacturing wafer has a different and unique processing history. Therefore, all fabricated IC's are different from one another. Some of them may be affected by process disturbances in such a way that they do not meet expected specifications. In some cases process instabilities may even cause only a small fraction of all fabricated IC's to have an acceptable performance; i.e. the manufacturing yield to be small.

In the remaining part of this section a couple of examples illustrating the relationship between random process instabilities and features of IC elements are discussed in more detail.

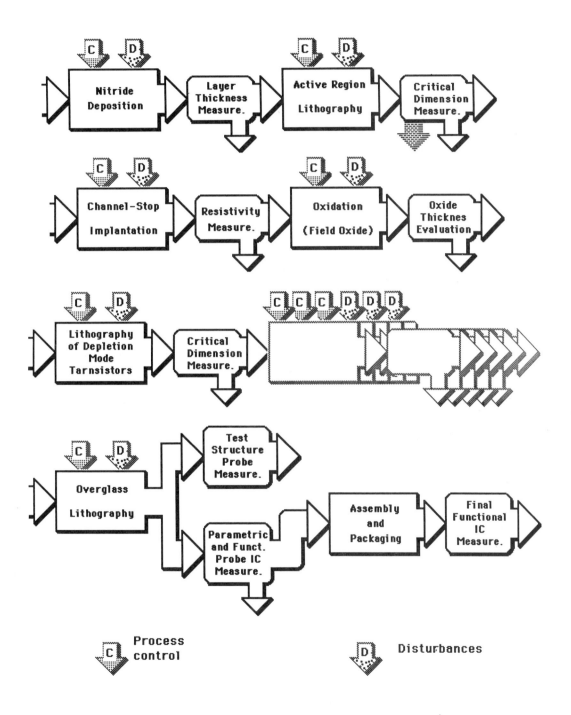

Figure 2-4: An example of the organization of the NMOS manufacturing process.

2.1.3.1. Process instabilities

There are many reasons for process instabilities. Some of them are illustrated in Fig. 2-5, Fig. 2-6, and Fig. 2-7.

A **line registration error**, which is defined as a difference between the location of an edge of the IC region in the design and in the actual IC, is a good example of a processing effect that is influenced by a lot of independent random disturbances.

Fig. 2-5 shows the contributions of various factors to the difference in the location of the diffusion region boundary in the actual IC and in the design. Note that some of the vectors in this drawing may contain a large random component. For instance, the length of the bird's beak may be disturbed by such factors as the amount of oxygen provided during field oxide growth, conditions of the Si-nitride interface, temperature fluctuations, and many others. The resist exposure and development error may be affected by UV light diffraction, the thickness of photoresist, and so on. Consequently, the location of the edge of the n^+ region fluctuates around its nominal value as determined by the design.

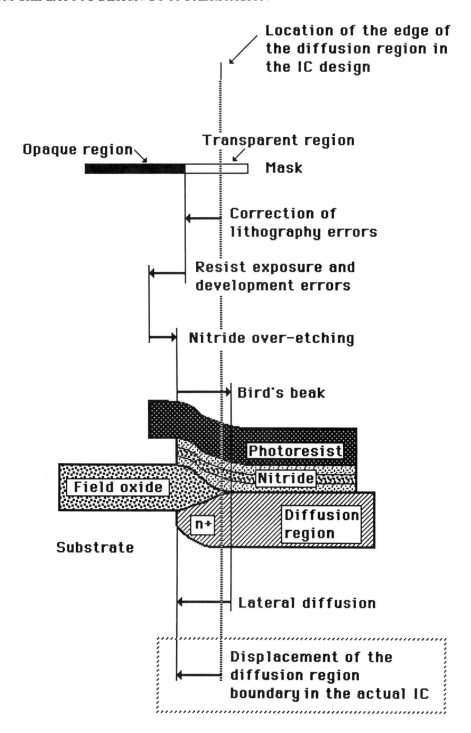

Figure 2-5:   Line registration errors in the location
of the diffusion region boundary.

Another source of random disturbances in the process is **mask misalignment**. It is caused by the limited precision with which subsequent lithography masks used in the process can be aligned with respect to layout features already engraved on the surface of the manufacturing wafer.

Consequences of mask misalignment are illustrated in Fig. 2-6, where differences between idealized and actual metal - polysilicon contacts are depicted. Note that the final misalignment error, causing a break in the metal-polysilicon connection, is caused by an accumulation of three alignment errors.

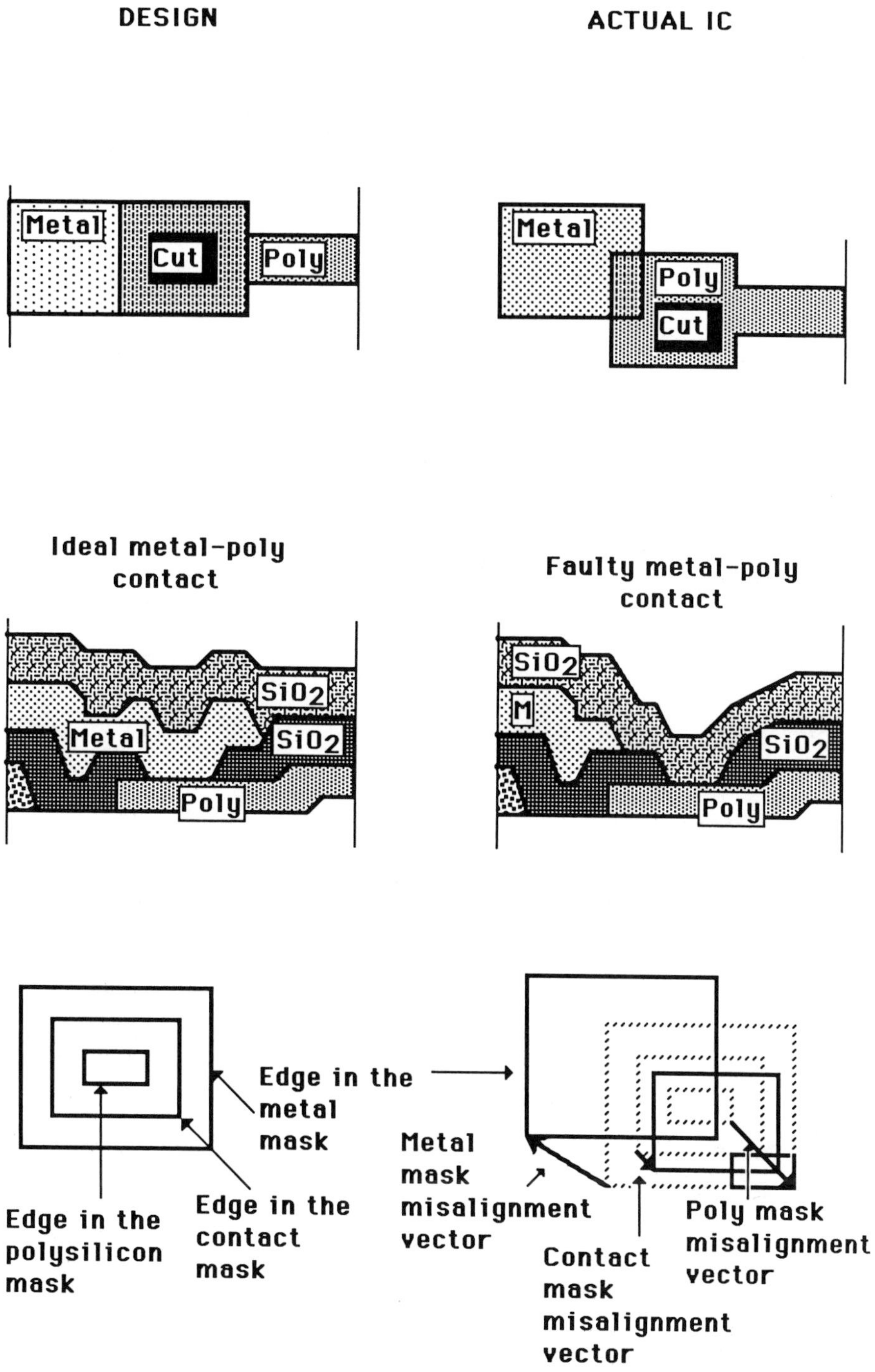

Figure 2-6: Misalignment of the metal, poly, and contact masks.

The horizontal dimensions of the IC device are not the only parameters that are affected by process instabilities. Fig. 2-7 shows an example of a disturbance that causes random fluctuation of threshold voltages of MOS transistors. In this case, the affected parameter is the thickness of the thin gate oxide which in the actual circuits varies from one location on the wafer to another. The gate oxide is also nonuniformly distributed within a single IC chip.

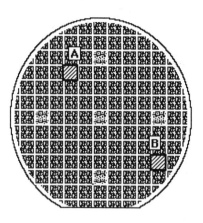

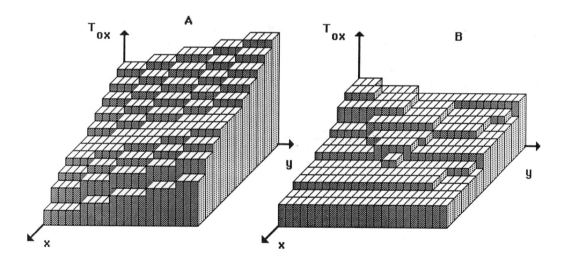

Figure 2-7: Variations of the gate oxide thickness among and within
IC chips at different locations of the wafer.

2.2. The process-design relationship

In IC design a prediction of an outcome of the manufacturing process is used to justify any design decision. Therefore, any design methodology is strongly affected by the designer's ability to predict manufacturing consequences of his or her decision.

The problem is that the outcome of the manufacturing process is modified by random disturbances that are inherent elements of any manufacturing process. Thus accurate prediction of the process behavior is not possible, and design decisions have to be made with a certain safety margin. This also means that any reasonable design methodology should take into account such differences as shown in Fig. 2-8, i.e. differences between concept used in the design and realities in the actual IC.

The next section explains how process-induced random deformations of the IC layout affect the methodology of layout design.

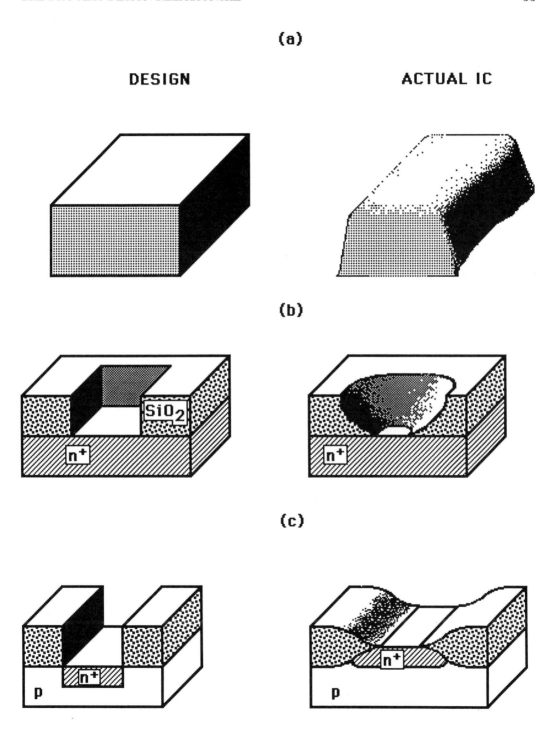

Figure 2-8: Discrepancies between concepts used in the design and actual elements of the IC, showing a metal line (a), contact cut (b), and diffusion region (c).

2.2.1. Geometrical design rules

To minimize chances that random deformations of the geometry of IC elements disturb functionality of the fabricated IC, the concept of **geometrical design rules** is utilized. This section explains how this concept has been developed and how it is related to the random process instabilities discussed in this chapter.

As was suggested in previous examples, locations of the edges of IC regions are disturbed by process instabilities. It can be proved that errors in the edge locations are normally distributed (see Fig. 2-9). Consequently, any distance between two edges in the actual IC is random and also normally distributed. The mean value of this distribution is a function of the nominal location of the region's edges in the design.

For normal operation of an IC it is required that regions that are separated in the design should remain separated in the actual IC. This means that all distances between edges of such regions in the actual IC should be greater than zero. This can be achieved if the **nominal distances** (distances in the IC design) are large enough to preserve the required spacing under the worst-case disturbances in the process.

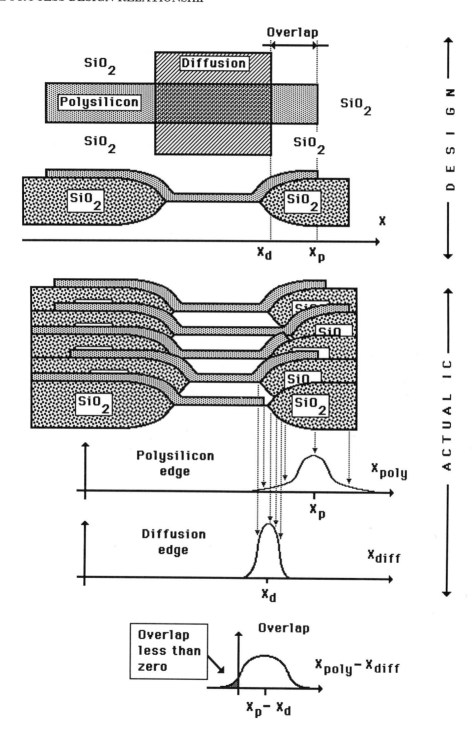

Figure 2-9: Minimal spacing between edges of two regions, determined by fluctuations in the location of the boundaries of these regions in the actual IC.

Thus, for each pair of edges in the design a minimal spacing can be defined such that in the actual IC the spacing between equivalent edges will be preserved. A set of spacings defined for a particular technology is called **geometrical design rules**. Fig. 2-10 shows an example of geometrical design rules for a typical n-channel MOS technology. They are defined as minimal acceptable distances between edges of various regions. In the case illustrated in the drawing, all rules are expressed in terms of the same number λ.

For some technologies design rules may be different from the rules presented in Fig. 2-10. In some cases they are much more complicated and take into account other than purely geometrical relationships. It is important to note that the design rules are established to eliminate sensitivity of IC topology to process instabilities. They determine the scale of integration of an IC and define specific features of the layout. These features are clearly seen when layouts of the circuits designed for different technologies are compared.

Drawings presented in the further part of this book have been created using some design rules. These rules are not discussed or presented, but it is important to remember that the final appearance of drawings presented in this book was decided by the design rules. In particular, the drawings presented in Chapter 4 were produced using a set of rules very similar to the rules introduced in Fig. 2-10.

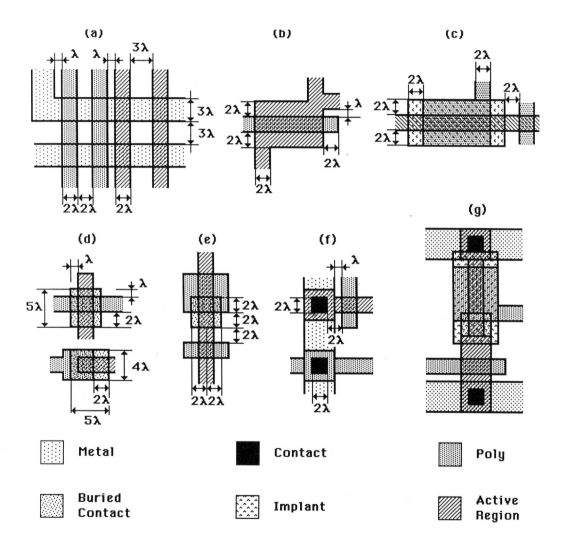

Figure 2-10: The set of geometrical design
rules for the NMOS technology.
The symbol λ represents a unit spacing.

Chapter 3
Bipolar Technology

with contributions from
David Greve

This chapter illustrates the fabrication of components in a junction-isolated bipolar process. **Junction isolation** means that individual components (resistors, transistors, capacitors) are isolated from each other by back-to-back p-n junctions. Since one of the two junctions is always reverse biased, no significant current can flow. Other isolation schemes will be illustrated in subsequent chapters.

3.1. The bipolar process

In the process description that follows, the result of completed process steps will be illustrated with solid lines; a "ghost" outline will show a superimposed completed device. The fabrication of an npn transistor will be shown in detail; only the completed device will be shown for other components.

For convenience, the illustrations will use different scales for horizontal and vertical dimensions. The vertical dimension is somewhat enlarged so that the junctions and film thicknesses are actually smaller than they appear. This is done so that all the important features can be seen in a drawing of reasonable size.

3.1.1. Fabrication steps

Fabrication begins with a lightly p-type doped substrate that is oxidized using a wet oxidation atmosphere and a high temperature thermal cycle. Next, a window is opened in an oxide layer using the **buried layer** (or **subcollector**) mask (Fig. 3-1 (a)). A heavy n-type diffusion is then performed (Fig. 3-1 (b)). After the diffusion, a step remains in the substrate due to the unequal thicknesses of oxide that have been grown.

The buried layer provides a low-resistance path from the active part of the transistor (just beneath the emitter window) to the collector contact some distance away. In order to minimize diffusion of the buried layer during subsequent processing, dopants with relatively small diffusion coefficients such as arsenic and antimony are used.

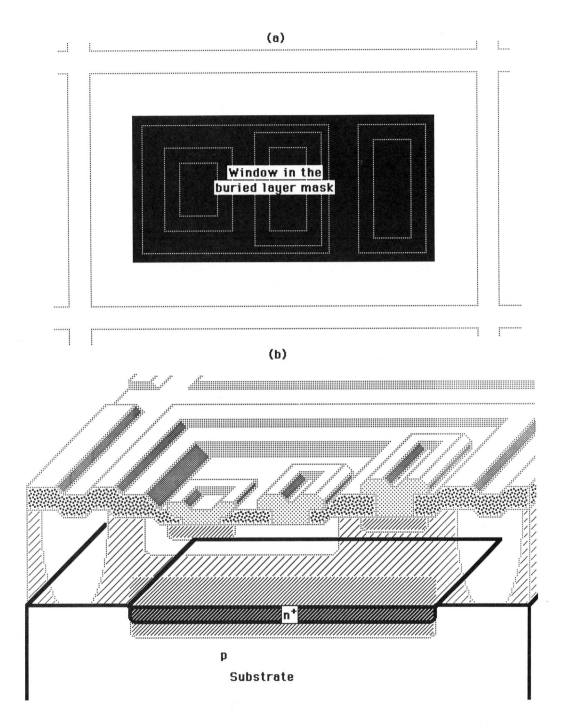

Figure 3-1: Diffusion of the buried layer. Segment of
the mask (a) and cross-section of
the npn transistor (b) after the diffusion .

No masking is needed for the next step in which a lightly doped n-type layer is grown on the entire wafer (Fig. 3-2 (a)). Under proper conditions, this single-crystal layer continues the crystal structure of the original wafer and is therefore suitable for fabrication of devices. (In contrast, polysilicon deposition is performed under conditions where the crystal structure is not continued and is therefore not suitable for fabrication of active devices.) The small step in the substrate remaining after the buried layer diffusion is replicated on the surface of the epitaxial film, so that subsequent mask levels can be aligned to the buried layer.

Deposition of the epitaxial layer is particularly critical because defects that occur when the structure of the underlying wafer is not exactly replicated will result in nonfunctioning devices.

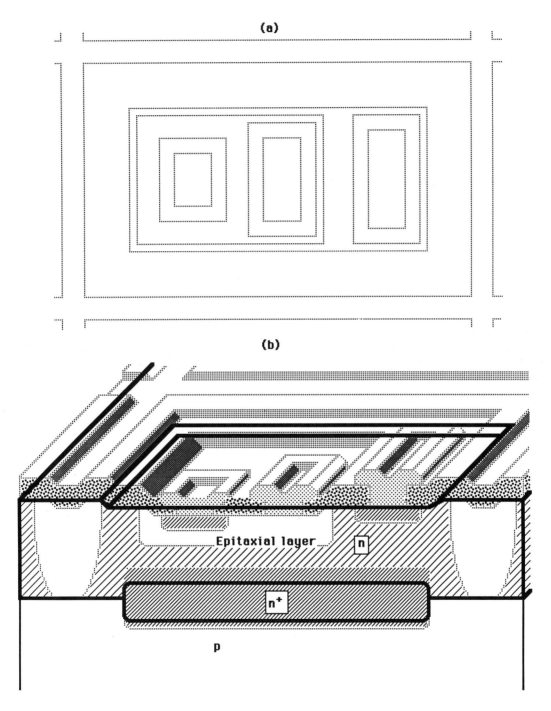

(a)

(b)

Epitaxial layer [n]

[n+]

p

Figure 3-2: Epitaxy. Segment of the mask (a) and cross-section of the npn transistor (b) after layer deposition.

In the subsequent steps isolated islands are formed. An oxide layer is grown on the substrate and a window for the **isolation diffusion** is opened (Fig. 3-3 (a)). A deep p-type diffusion is then performed. Subsequent high-temperature steps will cause the p isolation diffusion to reach as far as the original substrate surface. The result will be n-type islands completely surrounded by p-type material.

Note that these illustrations show the buried layer becoming wider during each process step. This is because both epitaxy and the isolation diffusion are high-temperature steps ($> 1000\,°C$) which cause diffusion of impurities already in the wafer.

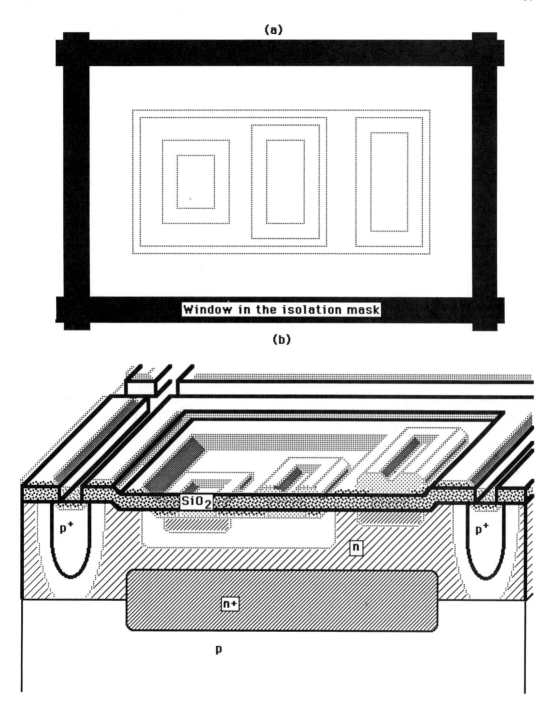

(a)

(b)

Window in the isolation mask

Figure 3-3: Island formation. Segment of the mask (a) and
cross-section of the npn transistor (b) after diffusion of
the p-type isolation.

Then the **base diffusion** mask is used to open a window in the oxide (Fig. 3-4 (a)). A p-type diffusion is performed to define the base of the transistor. Part of the diffusion process takes place in an oxidizing ambient so that there is an oxide layer over the entire wafer after the diffusion is completed.

Note that the base junction does not reach as far as the buried layer. Consequently the active part of the collector is lightly doped. This gives more ideal characteristics for the transistor and also a higher breakdown voltage.

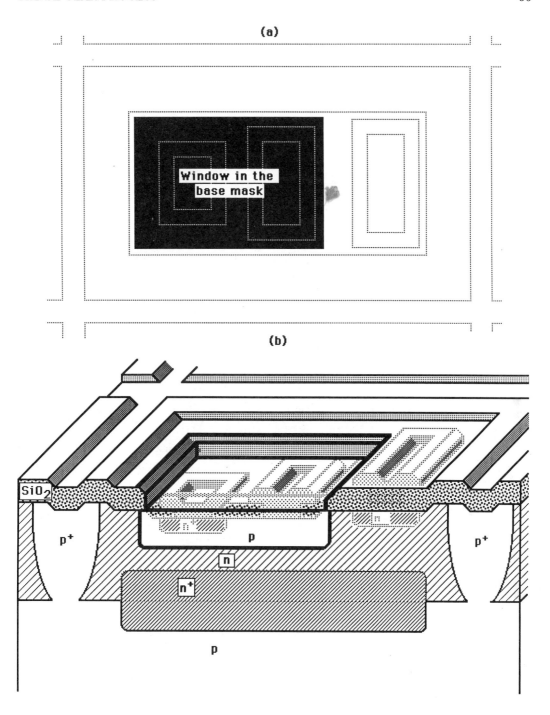

(a)

Window in the
base mask

(b)

SiO$_2$

p$^+$

n$^+$

p

n

n$^+$

p$^+$

p

Figure 3-4:   Transistor base p-type diffusion. Segment of the mask (a) and
cross-section of the npn transistor (b) after
base diffusion.

The **emitter mask** (Fig. 3-5 (a)) is next used to open a window for both the emitter diffusion (left window which lies within the base diffusion) and a collector contact (right window). A shallow, high-concentration n-type diffusion is performed. Again, this diffusion is performed in an oxidizing ambient so that oxide covers the entire wafer after the diffusion is completed. The diffusion is necessary for the collector contact since aluminum forms a rectifying contact to lightly doped n-type silicon.

It is instructive to compare the active area of the transistor to the total area required on the wafer. The current flow in the transistor is vertical so that the active area is just as large as the emitter window. However, the emitter window must be located within the base window (including alignment tolerances) and the base window needs to be located within the isolation diffusion. The area of the isolation diffusion is itself larger than the original mask opening since the isolation dopant diffuses laterally as well as vertically. Additional area is also required for the collector contact. Consequently, the active area is only a small fraction of the transistor area.

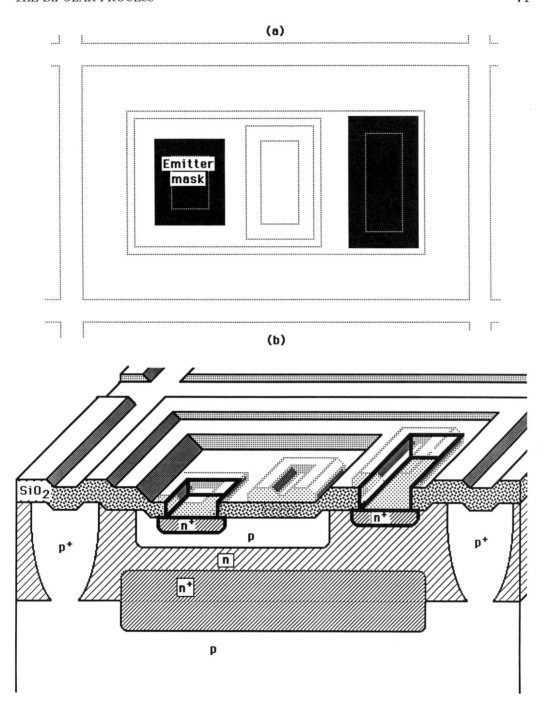

Figure 3-5: Emitter diffusion. Segment of the mask (a) and cross-section of the npn transistor (b) after emitter diffusion.

The **contact mask** is used to define windows within the emitter, base, and collector regions (Fig. 3-6 (a)). The cross-section after etching is shown in Fig. 3-6 (b).

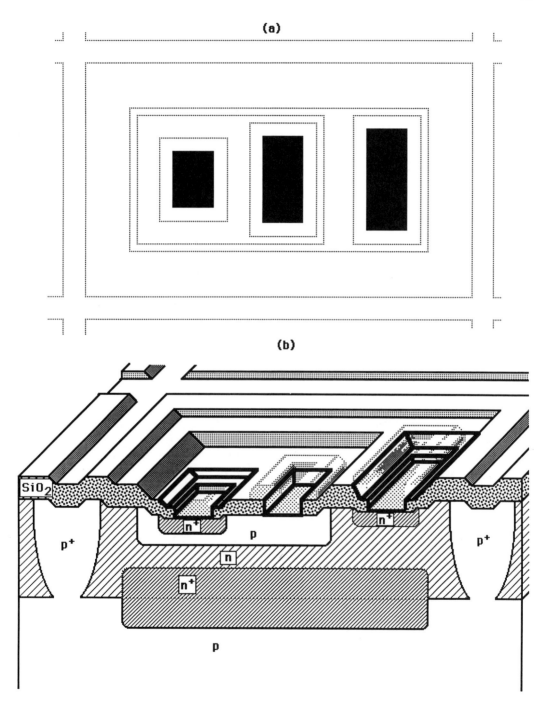

Figure 3-6: Contact etching. Segment of the mask (a) and
cross-section of the npn transistor (b) after
contact etching in the emitter, base, and collector regions.

Finally metal deposition and etching are performed. A layer of metal is first deposited over the entire wafer. The **metal mask** (Fig. 3-7 (a)) is then used to define photoresist which serves as a mask for metal etching. The cross-section after etching is shown in Fig. 3-7 (b). Metal lines (not shown) are used to connect various devices together to form a circuit.

The metallization mask is designed with sufficient overlap so that the metal covers the entire contact window. The most common metallization at present is aluminum or aluminum alloys. More complex metallization schemes are also used in order to prevent undesirable intermetallic reactions in the contact windows.

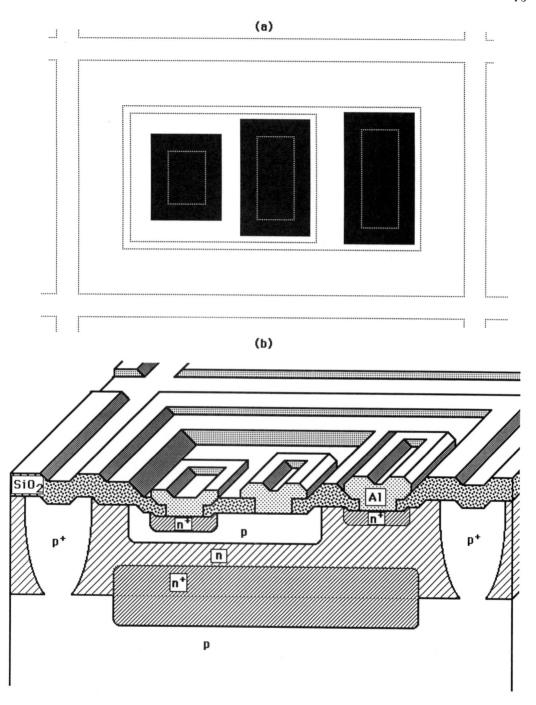

Figure 3-7: Metal deposition and etching. Segment of the mask (a) and cross-section of the npn transistor (b) after the metallization step.

The six mask levels needed to fabricate an npn transistor are illustrated together in Fig. 3-8 (a). The active area of the transistor (Fig. 3-8 (b)) is the area beneath the emitter mask (roughly 5% of the total area in this process). The remaining area is necessary for contacts and to guarantee the required overlaps.

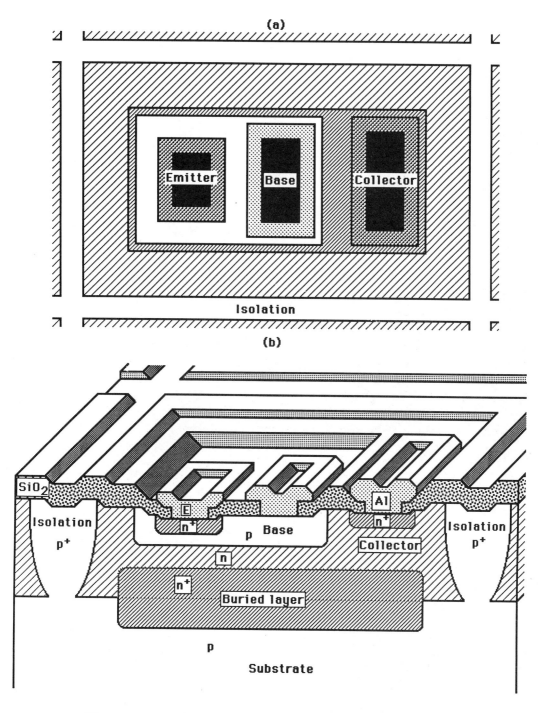

Figure 3-8: Layout (a) and cross-section of the complete npn transistor (b).

3.2. Bipolar devices

In this section, we illustrate the construction of other components (diodes, resistors, and pnp transistors) that can be made using the same bipolar transistor process. Since all these devices can be made simultaneously by appropriate design of the masks, all types of devices can be used in a circuit.

3.2.1. The npn transistor

In this section, we look in detail at the dopant profiles present in the **npn bipolar transistor** fabricated in a junction-isolated process.

Fig. 3-9 shows the dopant profiles beneath the emitter window in the npn transistor. The profiles are plotted on a logarithmic scale because of the wide range of dopant concentrations. Fig. 3-9(b) shows the dopant profiles for a typical analog integrated circuit process. In such a process, relatively high breakdown voltages are necessary. The collector-base breakdown voltage is determined by the doping level and thickness of the collector region. A high breakdown voltage is obtained by making the epitaxial layer lightly doped and sufficiently thick so that the base diffusion and the top of the buried layer diffusion are separated. Good current gain for the transistor is obtained by making the base region thin and less heavily doped than the emitter.

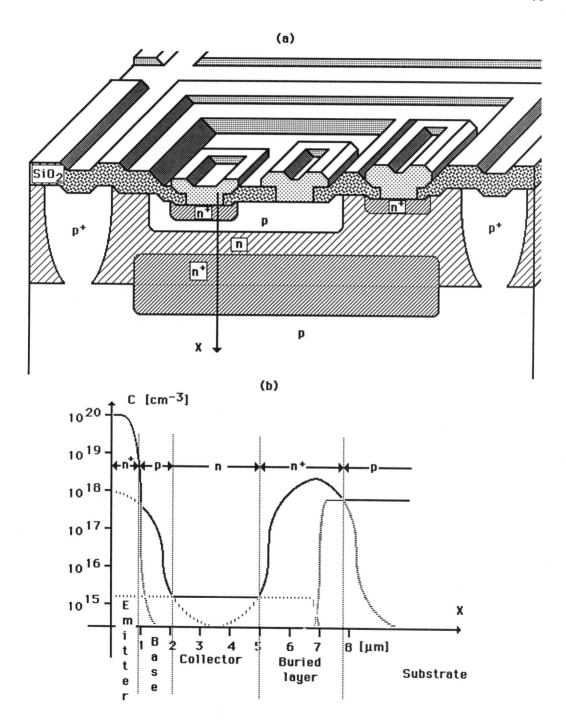

Figure 3-9: Cross-section of the npn transistor (a)
and impurity profile in the emitter region (b),
as indicated by the vertical arrow in (a).

Fig. 3-10 shows the impurity profile beneath the base. The dopant profile is shown in Fig. 3-10 (b). Note that the base current must flow laterally to the base contact through a resistive region formed by the base diffusion. This parasitic resistance can be reduced by using a heavier base diffusion (higher impurity concentration). This involves a tradeoff since increasing the base doping decreases the current gain.

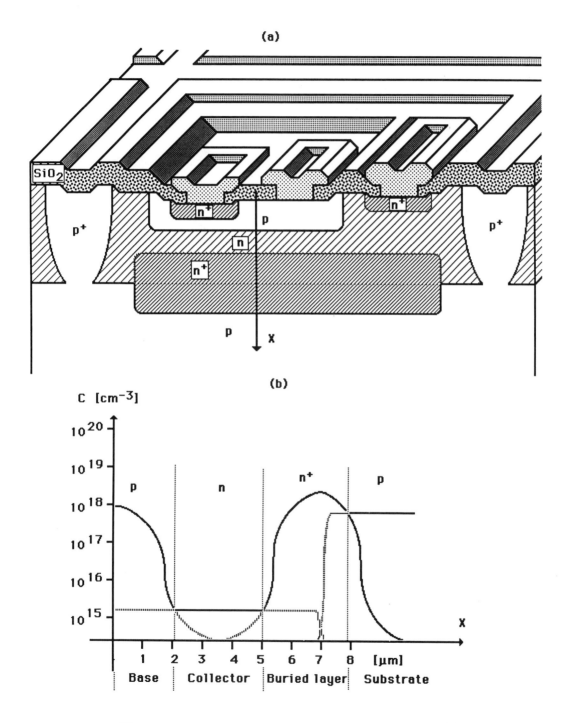

Figure 3-10: Cross-section of the npn transistor (a)
and impurity profile in the base region (b).

Fig. 3-11 shows the impurity profile beneath the collector contact. The dopant profile is shown in (b). The collector current must flow vertically from the buried layer to the heavily doped collector contact. The resistance of this portion of the lightly doped epitaxial layer is a major part of the collector resistance.

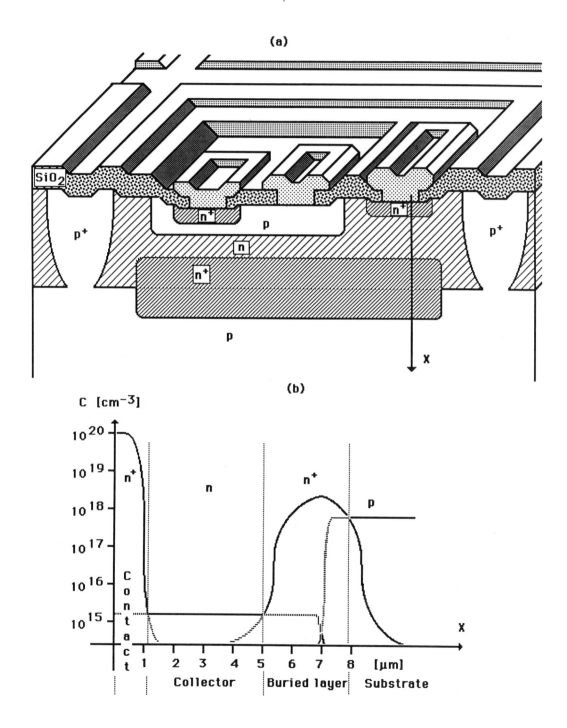

Figure 3-11: Cross-section of the npn transistor (a)
and impurity profile in the collector region (b).

The impurity profile of the isolation diffusion is shown in Fig. 3-12. A very deep diffusion is necessary so that the p region reaches all the way through the epitaxial layer to the substrate. This process requires long diffusion times and high temperatures.

(a)

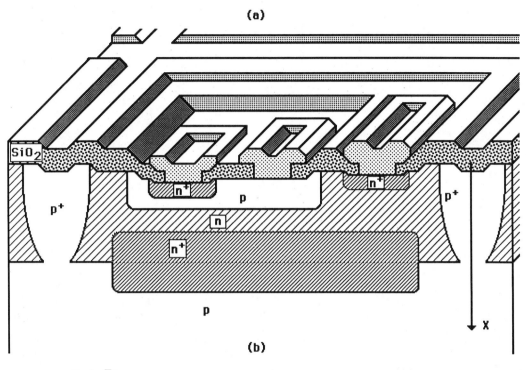

(b)

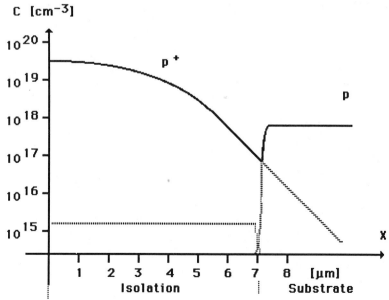

Figure 3-12: Cross-section of the npn transistor (a) and impurity profile in the isolation (b).

3.2.2. Diodes

A **diode** can be formed by using the metallization mask to **short** (connect together) the base and collector contacts (Fig. 3-13 (a)). A cross-section of the resulting diode is shown in Fig. 3-13 (b). This diode has a breakdown voltage close to that of the emitter-base junction (about 6 volts). Diodes can also be formed using a collector-base junction by shorting the base to the emitter or by using a collector-base junction alone. Regardless of the method used, the area occupied by a diode is equal to or at best slightly less than the area of a transistor.

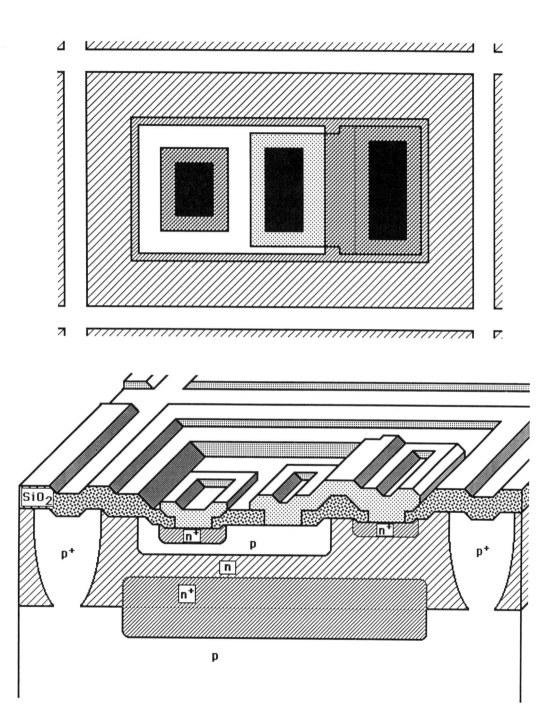

Figure 3-13: Layout (a) and cross-section of the diode, in this case a collector-base junction (b).

3.2.3. Resistors

Any isolated region with two contacts can be used as a **resistor**. The resistance is determined by the doping level of the region and the dimensions of the resistor; consequently, some ranges of resistor values are impractical because they take up too much area. In addition, integrated circuit resistors are not as ideal as discrete resistors. For example, the width of depletion layers depends on the voltage applied to the resistor. All integrated circuit resistors therefore exhibit voltage dependent (or nonlinear) behavior.

3.2.3.1. The base resistor

A base diffusion with two contacts forms one type of resistor. The resistor is formed in a separate isolation island so that it is independent of other devices on the chip. The resistivity of the base diffusion is usually determined during the design of the npn transistor. Different values of resistors can only be obtained by changing the width of the resistor or the distance between contacts.

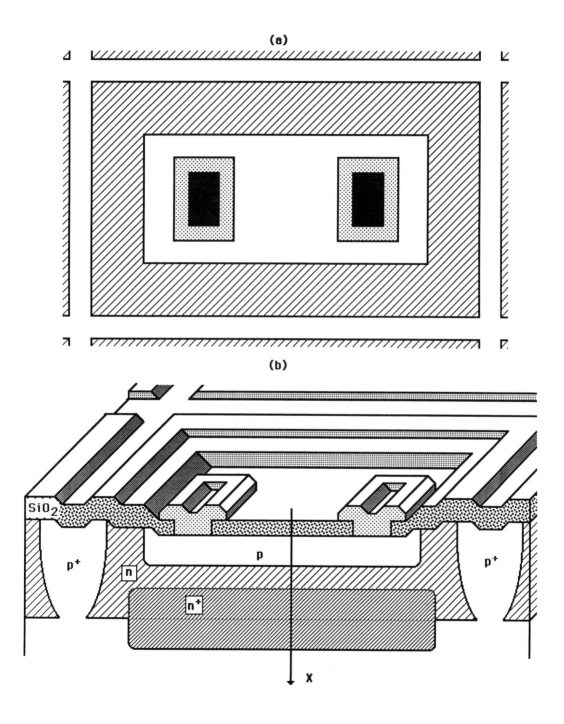

Figure 3-14: Layout (a) and cross-section (b) of the base resistor.

The resistance is determined by the ratio between the length and width of the resistor. For a given base diffusion, the resistance is given by $R = R_s (l/w)$, where l is the length of the resistor, w its width, and R_s (which has the dimensions of ohms) is the square resistance. R_s is called the square resistance since the ratio l/w is the number of squares, laid end to end, which make up the resistor.

(a)

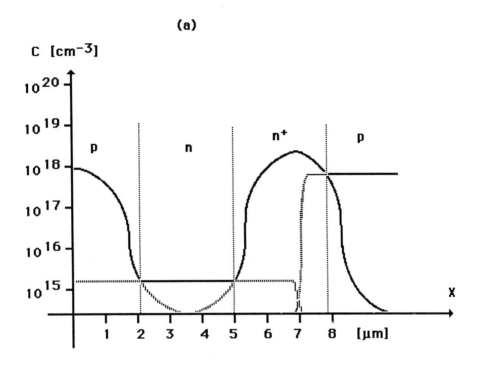

(b)

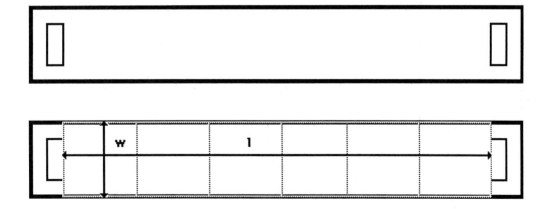

$$R = R_S \cdot l/w$$

Figure 3-15:   Impurity profile (a) and an equivalent number of
squares of the diffused resistor (b).

3.2.3.2. The emitter resistor

A resistor can also be fabricated by making an emitter diffusion with contacts at both ends. Since the emitter diffusion is heavier (larger dopant concentration) the square resistivity is lower.

(a)

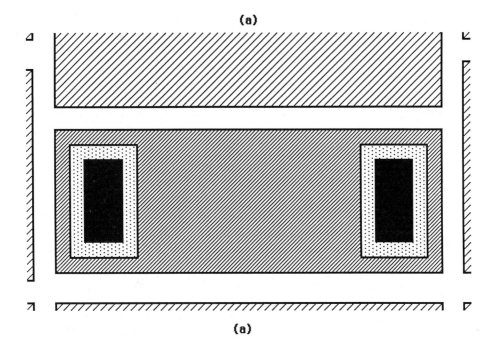

(a)

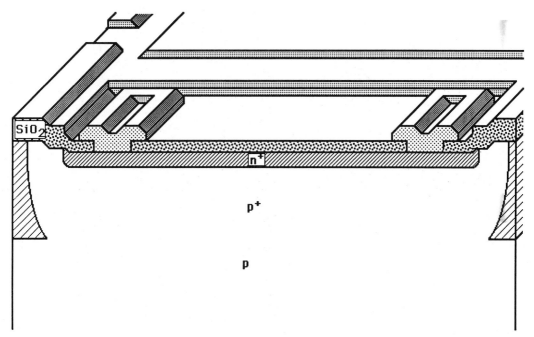

Figure 3-16: Layout (a) and cross-section (b) of the emitter resistor.

3.2.3.3. The epitaxial resistor

A resistor is fabricated by making two contacts to the epitaxial layer. Since the epitaxial layer is lightly doped, large resistor values are possible. The buried layer must be omitted to obtain such large resistor values.

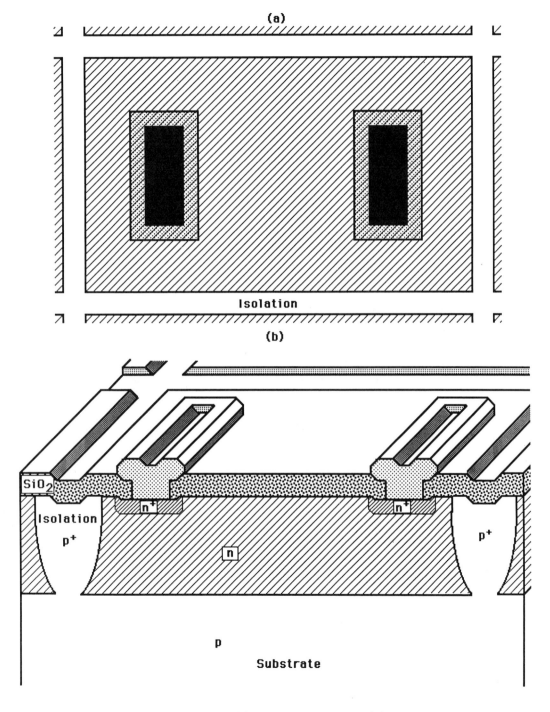

Figure 3-17:   Layout (a) and cross-section (b) of the epitaxial
resistor.

3.2.3.4. The pinch resistor

The **pinch resistor** is similar to a base resistor, but an emitter diffusion is used to reduce the thickness of the resistor. Since the emitter diffusion "covers up" the most heavily doped portion of the base, very large resistor values can be obtained this way. Pinch resistors exhibit a relatively strong dependence on bias since a change in potential modulates the depletion layer thickness and therefore changes the base width.

(a)

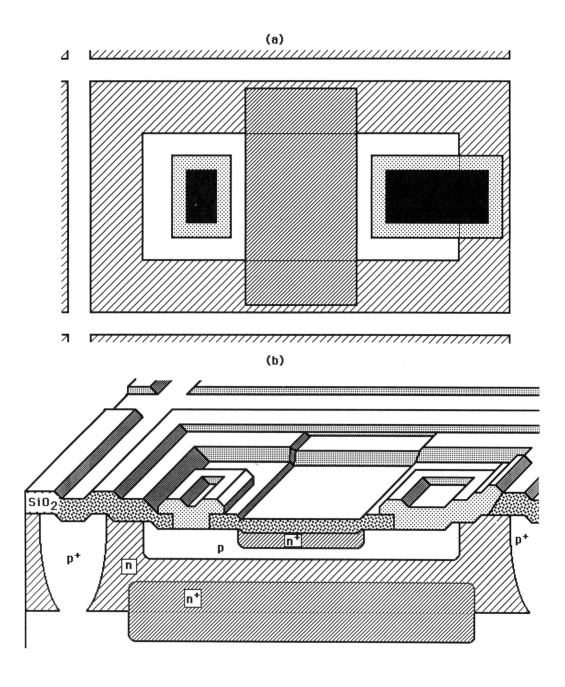

(b)

Figure 3-18:   Layout (a) and cross-section (b) of the pinch
resistor.

3.2.4. PNP transistors

Bipolar integrated circuit processes are designed in order to optimize the performance of npn transistors. The same sequence can be used, however, to fabricate pnp transistors with somewhat inferior characteristics. In this section, we illustrate the fabrication of two different varieties of pnp transistors.

3.2.4.1. The substrate pnp transistor

One type of pnp transistor is formed by using the p base diffusion as an emitter. Fig. 3-19 (a) shows the mask layout. The epitaxial layer becomes the base and the p-type substrate is used as the collector (Fig. 3-19 (b)). Note the absence of the buried layer in this structure. Relatively good transistors can be made in this way (current gain of order 100) but the collectors of all substrate pnp transistors are connected to the substrate so that flexibility in circuit design is limited. The substrate is connected to the most negative potential in the circuit to ensure isolation of the devices on the chip.

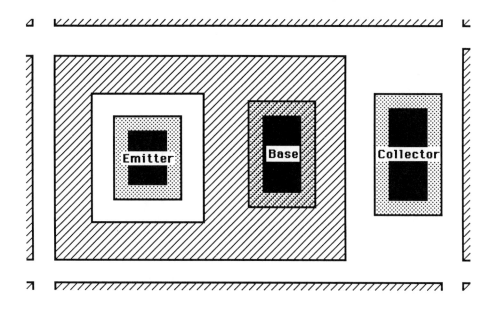

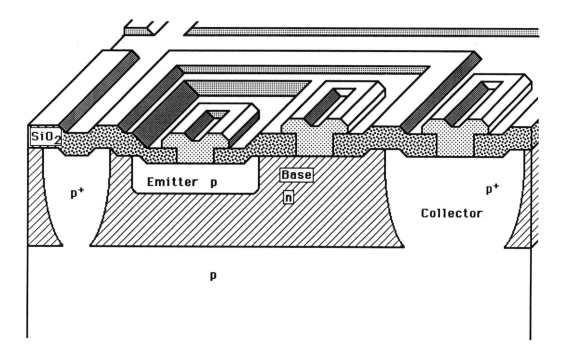

Figure 3-19:   Layout (a) and cross-section (b) of the pnp
substrate transistor.

3.2.4.2. The lateral pnp transistor

A pnp transistor can also be formed using one p diffusion as an emitter and one p diffusion as a collector. The epitaxial region is the base as before. This transistor has relatively poor current gain since the base thickness is determined by the minimum allowable separation between base diffusions. This separation is considerably greater than the base thickness in npn transistors, which is determined by a diffusion step.

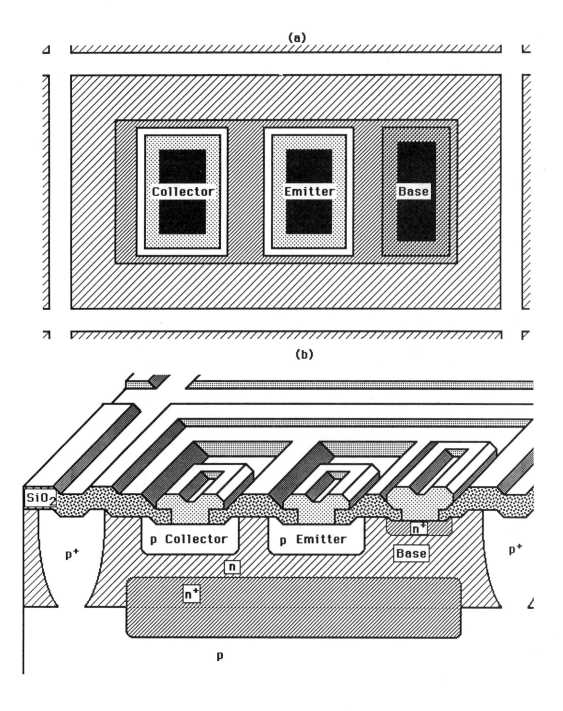

Figure 3-20: Layout (a) and cross-section (b) of the pnp lateral transistor.

3.3. Segments of the IC layout

3.3.1. Actual bipolar IC elements

All integrated circuit devices must be fabricated within isolation islands. During design, one must choose not only the electrical arrangement of the devices to form a circuit but also the physical layout of the devices on the chip. During the design process, devices are arranged in a way which minimizes circuit area and parasitics. One way to minimize area is to place several devices within the same isolation island where this is possible. For example, several base resistors can be placed within the same isolation island.

Fig. 3-21 shows a collection of resistors arranged so that several resistors share an isolation island where possible. For example, the network formed by base resistors R1, R2, and R3 shares an isolated island with the series connection of base resistor R4 and base pinch resistor R5. Since contacts take up a significant area, a savings in area is obtained by sharing contacts where feasible. Note that the epitaxial resistor R8 and emitter resistor R6 require separate isolated islands because all n regions within an island would be connected together. Base resistor R7 is drawn in a separate isolation island although in principle it could be included in the same island as R1- R5. In a practical circuit, separate islands might be used so that a resistor could be located close to other devices to simplify the metal interconnect pattern (not shown in this Figure).

Note that two of the isolation islands (R1-R5 and R7) include an extra contact to the epitaxial layer. This is necessary because otherwise the epitaxial layer would have an unpredictable bias. Such contacts would be connected to a fixed bias in the circuit.

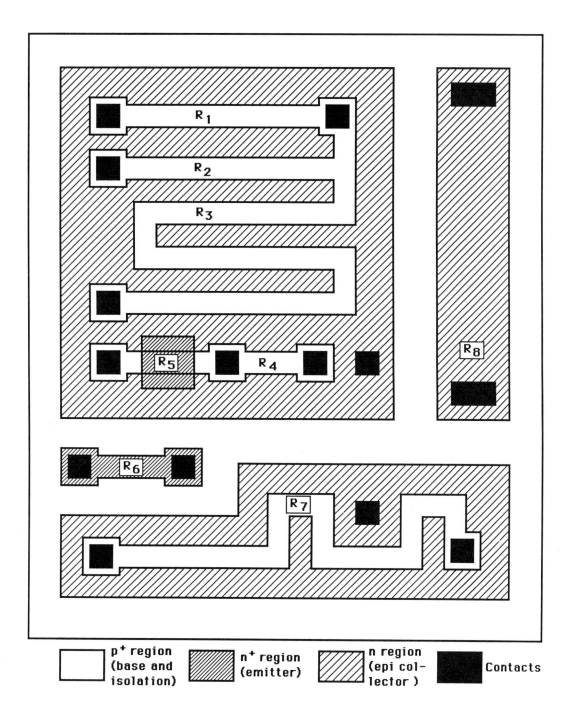

Figure 3-21: Examples of various resistors.

Transistors may be designed differently from those illustrated earlier depending upon the circuit application. For example, Fig. 3-22(a) shows an npn transistor with a larger emitter area. Such a transistor might be used where large output currents are required. Fig. 3-22(b) shows a lateral pnp transistor in which the collector area is much larger than the emitter area. This design results in somewhat better characteristics than those of the simplest transistor design since the injected minority carriers are collected more efficiently. Finally, Fig. 3-22(c) shows an npn transistor with two emitters. Such devices are commonly used in some varieties of logic circuits.

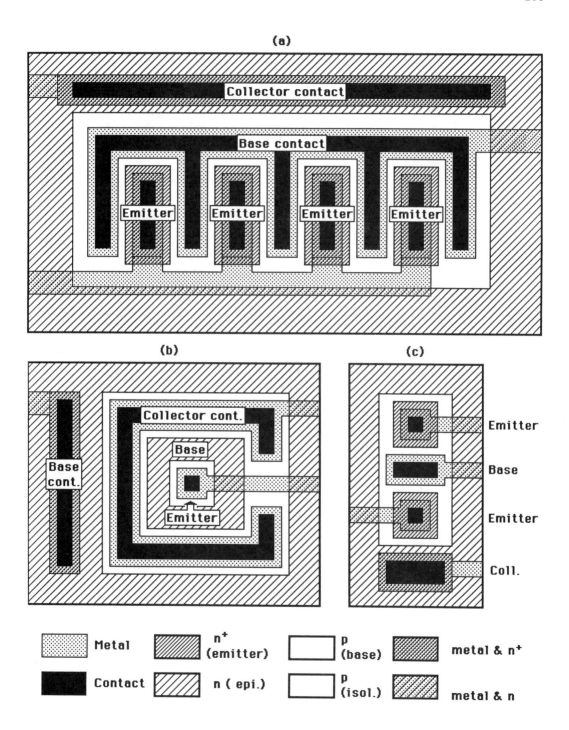

Figure 3-22: Examples of different npn and pnp transistors.

3.3.2. Segments of the layout[*]

In this section, mask drawings for a typical bipolar subcircuit are illustrated. The composite drawing of all mask levels is drawn using dotted lines, and each drawing shows the regions influenced by a particular process step as solid areas. For example, solid areas in Fig. 3-24 show the regions which receive the n^+ buried layer doping. Careful examination of these drawings allows us to reconstruct the original circuit diagram. The actual original circuit diagram is shown in Fig. 3-30 for comparison.

---

[*]The masks shown in Fig. 3-23 through Fig. 3-29 have been extracted from the drawing presented in A. G. Glaser and G. E. Subak-Sharpe, *Integrated Circuit Engineering - Design Fabrication and Applications (Addison-Wesley Publishing Company, 1977)* on page 327.

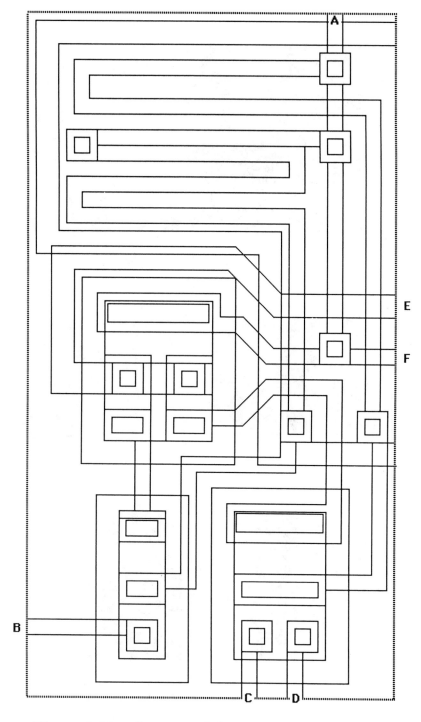

Figure 3-23: Segments of the composite drawing of the RS flip-flop.

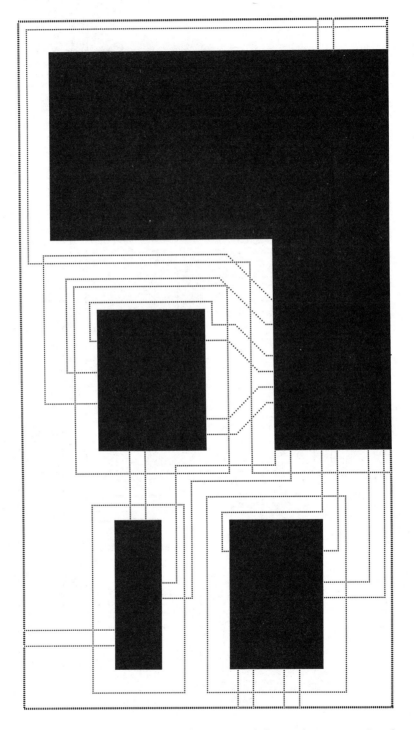

Figure 3-24: Buried layer mask extracted from the composite drawing
depicted in Fig. 3-23.

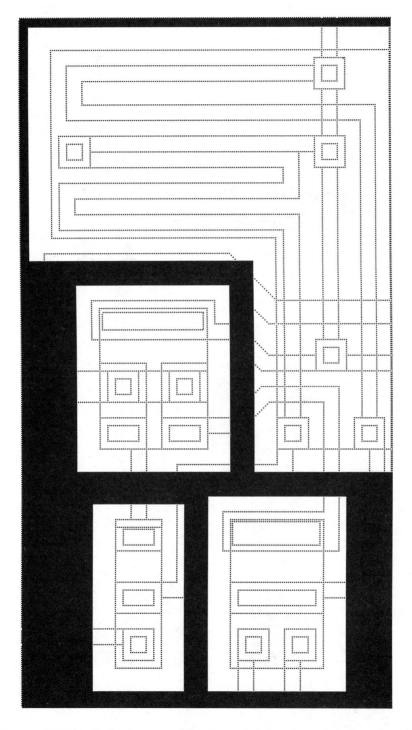

Figure 3-25: Isolation mask extracted from the composite drawing depicted in Fig. 3-23.

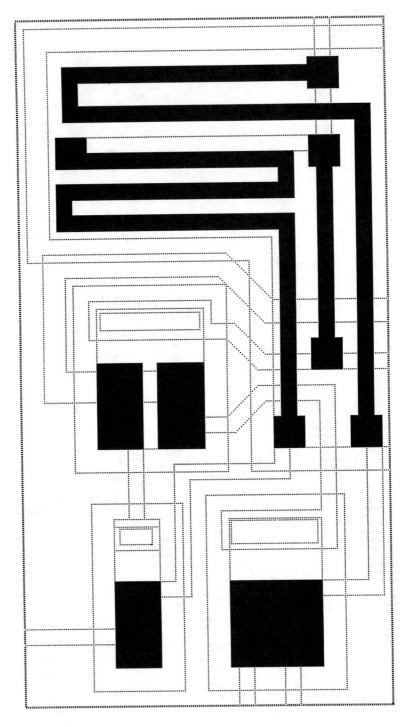

Figure 3-26: Base diffusion mask extracted from the composite drawing
depicted in Fig. 3-23.

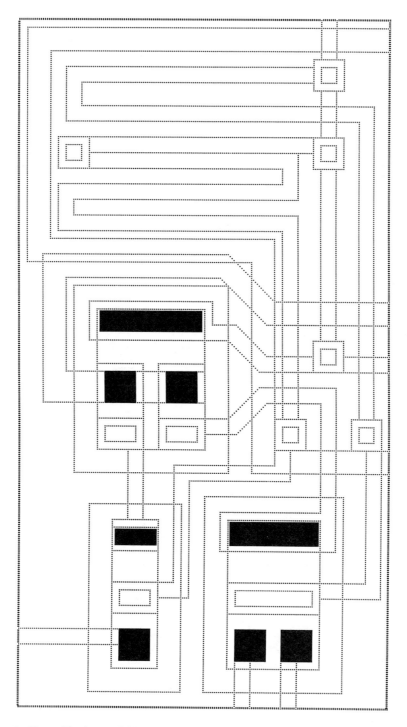

Figure 3-27: Emitter diffusion mask extracted from the composite drawing depicted in Fig. 3-23.

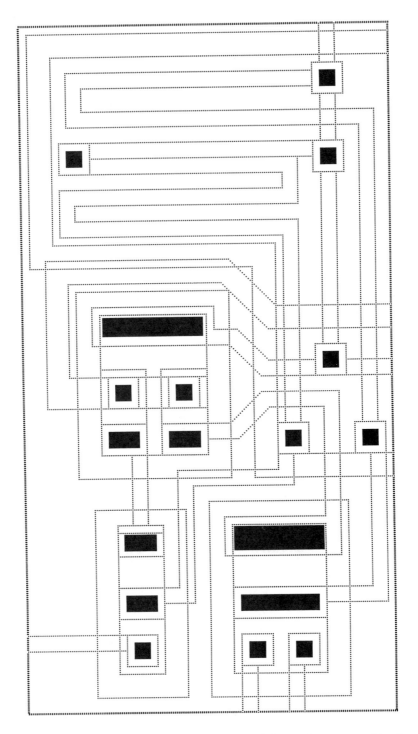

Figure 3-28:   Contact cuts mask extracted from the composite drawing
depicted in Fig. 3-23.

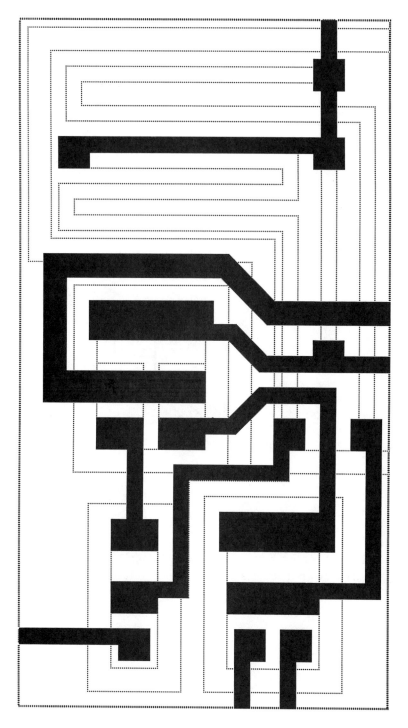

Figure 3-29: Metallization mask extracted from the composite drawing depicted in Fig. 3-23.

Fig. 3-30 shows the circuit diagram which is implemented in the mask drawings on the previous pages (Fig. 3-23 - Fig. 3-29).

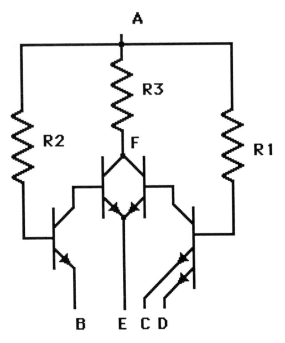

Figure 3-30:   Circuit diagram of the RS flip-flop depicted in Fig. 3-23.

Layout information also allows us to estimate the resistor values in a circuit. For example, Fig. 3-31 shows that the base resistors in the circuit have different numbers of squares and therefore different resistor values. We find by counting the squares that R2 $\approx$ R1 > R3. If information about the process (R_s) is available, the actual values of the resistors can be calculated.

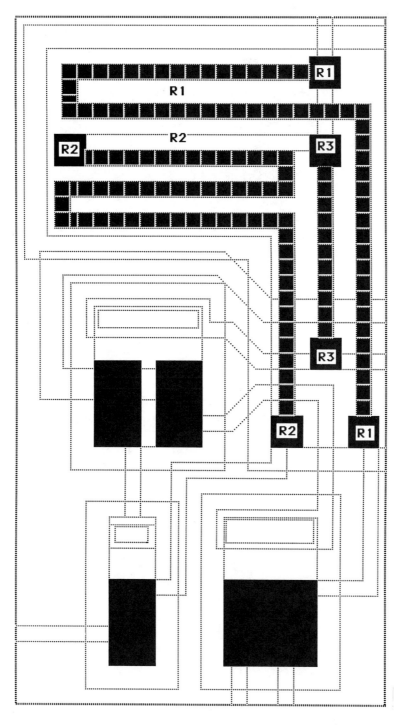

Figure 3-31: Base diffusion mask extracted from the composite drawing
depicted in Fig. 3-23, with squares inscribed into
the base diffusion resistors.

Chapter 4
NMOS Technology

with contributions from
Marek Syrzycki

This chapter describes standard **n-channel MOS technology (NMOS)** that uses both

1. Enhancement mode transistors with a positive threshold voltage, and

2. Depletion mode transistors with a negative threshold voltage.

These transistors are used as drivers, loads, and pass transistors to design arbitrary functional blocks. The NMOS process also provides three separate conductive layers, which can be used as internal connections in the circuit.

In this chapter we present a sequence of processing steps, describe the unique features of the NMOS elements, and show several examples of NMOS cells.

4.1. Description of the NMOS polysilicon gate technology

To explain the basic processing steps of the NMOS process in this section we will use drawings of an **Enhancement-Depletion (E-D) inverter.** This inverter consists of only two n-channel MOS transistors: an enhancement mode transistor and a depletion mode transistor. The layout of such an inverter will be shown in the upper part (labeled as (a)) of most of the ten subsequent drawings. Most of these drawings also show the shape of the mask or the layout region which is created by the given processing step. In NMOS technology p-type high-resistivity silicon wafers are used as the substrate material. The dopant level at the surface of the wafers is controlled by the boron ions implantation step, which is the first step in the process. This step provides for precise adjustment of threshold voltages of MOS transistors.

The goal of the second step (shown in Fig. 4-1 and Fig. 4-2) is to define regions in which MOS transistors will be created. These regions, called **active regions**, are created (Fig. 4-1) by:

1. Oxidation of the surface of the wafer (producing a SiO_2 layer);

2. Si_3N_4 deposition;

3. Photoresist deposition; and

4. Exposure and development of photoresist.

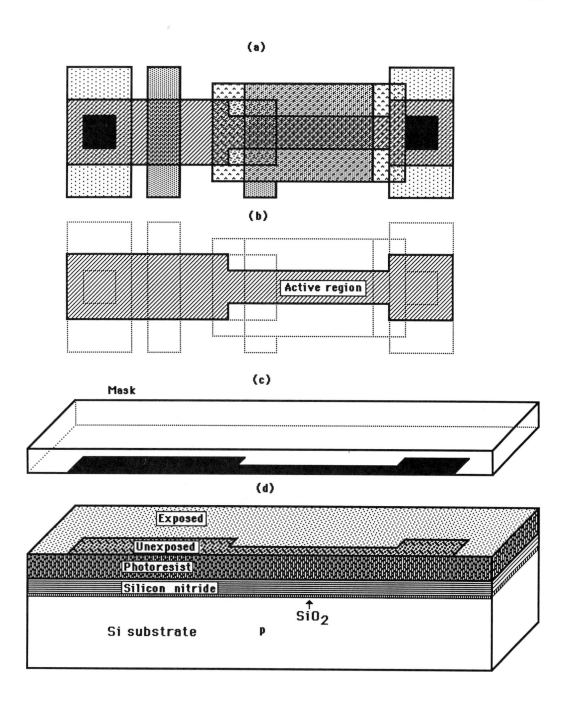

Figure 4-1: Patterning of the active region of the E-D inverter. Composite drawing of the layout (a), window in the mask (b), cross-section of the mask (c), and fabricated IC structure (d).

After development of the photoresist, the outlines of the active region are engraved on the surface of the silicon nitride because an undeveloped layer of photoresist in the shape of the active region remains on the silicon nitride (Fig. 4-2 (a)). Next, the wafer is treated with a reactant that etches the nitride. Areas covered with photoresist remain unetched (Fig. 4-2 (b)). Thus, after removal of the photoresist the surface of the wafer is covered with a thin layer of nitride that is also in the shape of the active region in the mask (Fig. 4-2 (c)).

(a)

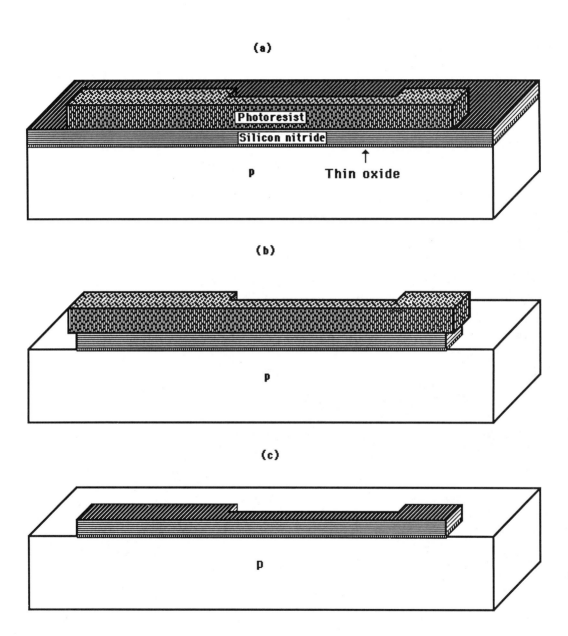

(b)

(c)

Figure 4-2: Patterning the silicon nitride layer. E-D inverter
cross-sections after: photoresist development (a),
etching of the nitride layer (b), and
stripping the photoresist (c).

In the next step another boron implantation (Fig. 4-3 (a)) is performed to create **channel-stop regions**. The channel-stop implant (p^+ in the Figure) prevents a channel from forming outside the active region. The silicon nitride layer now acts as a mask for the boron ions.

An oxidation step is then performed to grow a thick dioxide layer (0.6-0.8 μm) (Fig. 4-3 (b)). During this operation oxygen penetrates beneath the edges of the silicon nitride layer, forming the characteristic bird's beak shape of the oxide layer near the active region edge. At the same time boron diffuses deeper so the p^+ region is still under the thick field oxide.

After forming the field oxide the silicon nitride mask is removed (Fig. 4-3 (c)), and the active region is exposed for further operations.

Note that in the above sequence of steps we were able to affect two regions using one photomask.

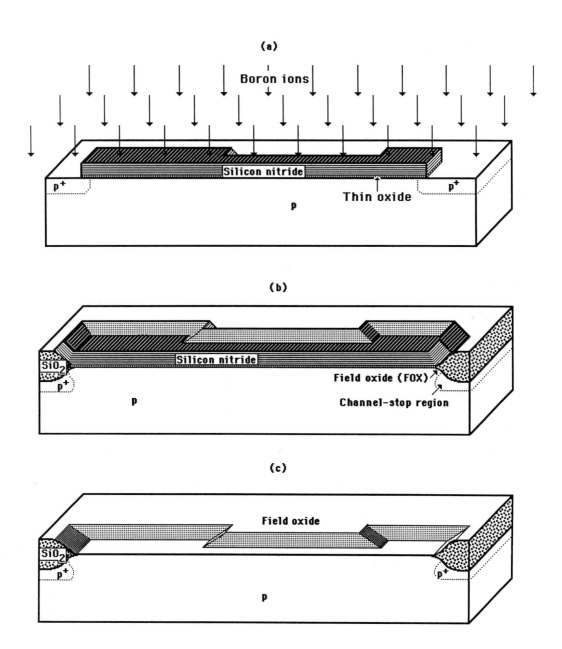

Figure 4-3: Active region formation and channel-stop implant. Implantation (a), is followed by oxidation (b), which leads to the formation of the active region (c). The implanted channel-stop is labeled p^+.

The goal of the implantation step shown in Fig. 4-4 is to modify the threshold voltage of the **depletion mode transistor**. Such transistors are used in circuits as loads and therefore they should have negative threshold voltages. A negative threshold voltage can be achieved by implanting n dopant into the p-type Si substrate. Thus in the step shown in Fig. 4-4 the photoresist layer is used to cover all the regions outside the channel of the depletion transistor. The implanted ions cannot penetrate into the substrate through the photoresist and the field oxide (see Fig. 4-4 (c)), so the location of the **depletion transistor channel** is defined by the intersection of the mask implantation window and the active region.

After the implantation step the photoresist layer is stripped off.

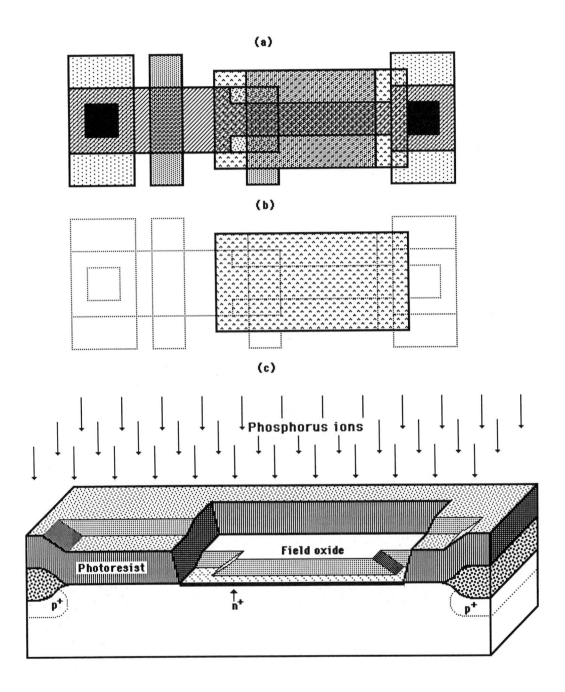

(a)

(b)

(c)

Phosphorus ions

Field oxide

Photoresist

p^+

n^+

p^+

Figure 4-4: Implantation of the channel of the depletion mode transistor in the E-D inverter. Composite drawing of the layout (a), window in the mask (b), and cross-section (c). n^+ represents the implanted dopant.

The subsequent processing step is **gate oxidation.** A thin oxide is grown only in the exposed active region. During this step the field oxide thickness is almost unchanged, since the thick oxide limits diffusion of oxygen atoms to the wafer surface (see Section 1.2.1).

Note now that to create a transistor a polysilicon layer will be deposited on top of the thin oxide. Thus, polysilicon and substrate will be isolated from each other unless a special contact cut is created in the gate oxide. The goal of the processing step illustrated in Fig. 4-5 is to create a connection between the polysilicon and the substrate, called **buried contact.**

To this end gate oxidation is followed by buried contact photolithography. The mask window pattern is shown in Fig. 4-5 (b). The oxides are etched from the region inside the mask window, thus uncovering the silicon surface in the region common to the buried contact window and the active region. The parts of the field oxide which are covered by the buried contact window will be only slightly etched (see Fig. 4-5 (c)).

(a)

(b)

(c)

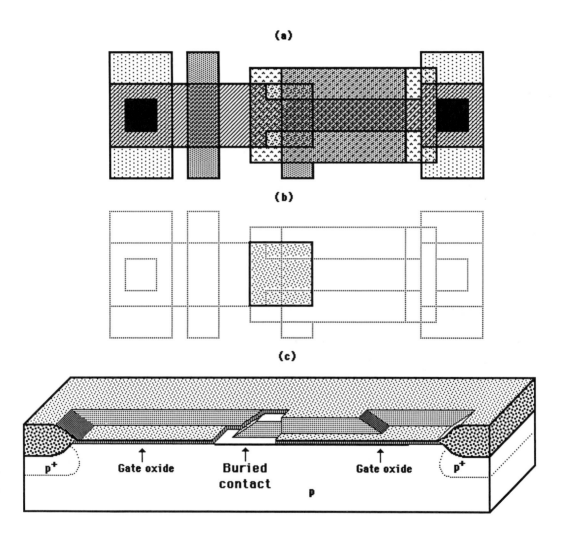

Figure 4-5: Buried contact etching in the E-D inverter.
Composite drawing of the layout (a), window
in the mask (b), and cross-section (c).

In the next step a polycrystalline silicon layer is deposited, and the fourth photolithographic mask is used to create transistor gates and connections (Fig. 4-6 (b)). The shaded mask windows indicate areas where the polysilicon will not be removed. After etching the polysilicon a different solvent is used to etch the gate oxide. Consequently, the part of the active region not covered with polysilicon is exposed for further processing.

Note that at this stage of the process transistor structures can be seen (Fig. 4-6 (c)). The polysilicon layer on top of the gate oxide forms the gate electrodes of MOS transistors. The polysilicon lines on the field oxide form interconnections. Finally, polysilicon which is both inside the buried contact window and inside the active region forms a contact between polysilicon and the silicon substrate.

(a)

(b)

(c)

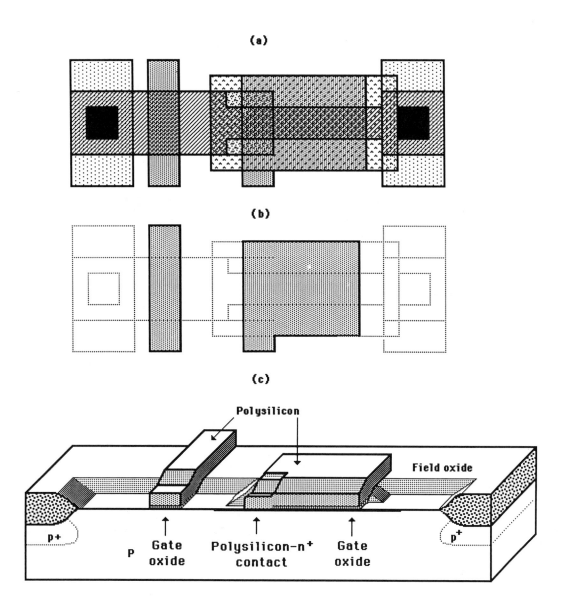

Polysilicon

Field oxide

p+

P

Gate oxide

Polysilicon-n+ contact

Gate oxide

p+

Figure 4-6: Patterning of the polysilicon layer followed by gate oxide etching in the E-D inverter. Composite drawing of the layout (a), window in the mask (b), and cross-section (c).

The goal of the next processing step is to form **drain and source n$^+$ regions.** A thick CVD donor-doped silicon oxide layer is deposited on the surface of the wafer (Fig. 4-7 (c)). This layer serves as a source of donor atoms. The high-temperature drive-in process which immediately follows CVD deposition forms n$^+$ regions where the active area is not covered with polysilicon or field oxide. These regions are shown in Fig. 4-8 (c).

Note that at the same time the polysilicon is doped as well, thus reducing its resistivity (typically to 15-40 Ω per square). Inside the buried contact donors diffuse from the CVD oxide through polysilicon into the substrate, thus creating a contact between the n$^+$ diffusion and polysilicon.

The sources and drains are fabricated using the field oxide and polysilicon as a mask, and therefore sources and drains are self-aligned with the gates.

The doped CVD oxide is useful as a dielectric layer and is not removed after the drive-in.

(a)

(b)

(c)

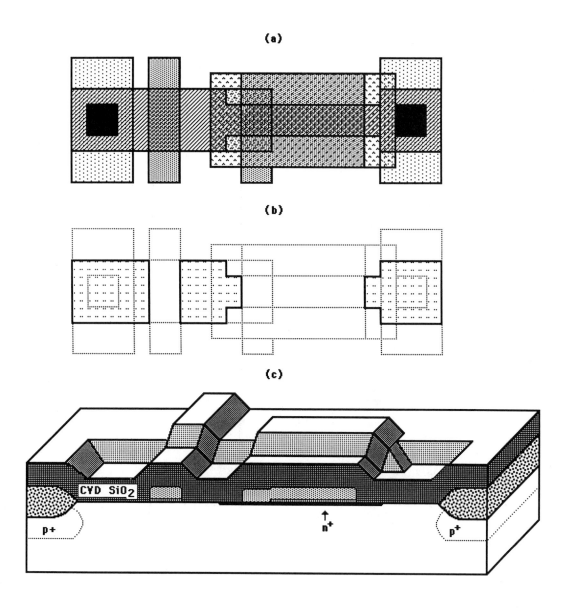

Figure 4-7: Deposition of the CVD SiO_2 layer followed by the diffusion of the drain and source regions. Composite drawing of the layout (a), regions in which impurities from the doped oxide can diffuse into the substrate (b), and cross-section (c).

In NMOS technology three layers are used for interconnections:

- n^+ diffusion in the p-type substrate,

- n^+ doped polysilicon, and

- metal (Al) lines.

These layers are isolated by oxide layers. Therefore, to create connections between conducting layers the oxide must be removed in those regions where contacts between the interconnection layers are necessary.

The goal of the fifth photolithographic step (Fig. 4-8) is to open holes through the oxide above the n^+ and polysilicon regions, thus providing for Al-n^+ and Al-polysilicon contacts.

In Fig. 4-8 (b) only an Al-n^+ contact cut is shown; Al-polysilicon contacts are shown elsewhere (e.g. in Fig. 4-21).

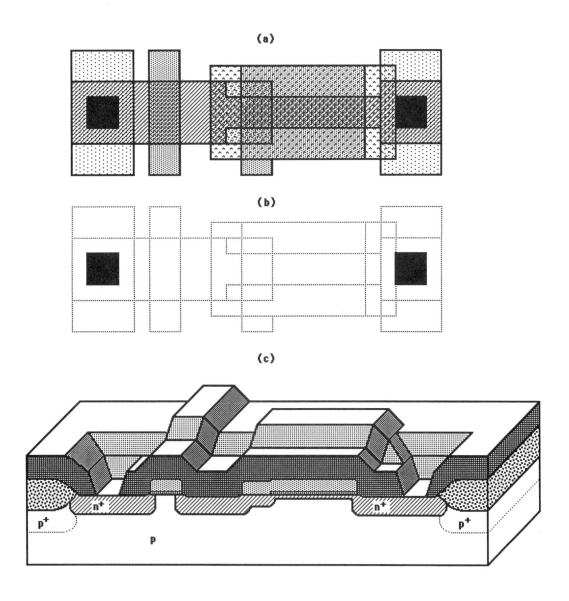

Figure 4-8: Contact cuts of the E-D inverter. Composite drawing of the layout (a), windows in the mask (b), and cross-section (c).

The last processing step in standard NMOS technology is the deposition and patterning of the metallization layer (Fig. 4-9). Vacuum-deposited aluminum is most commonly used for this purpose. The sputtered Al layer is a highly conductive material. This layer is used for most interconnections in the circuit, especially those which carry large amounts of supply current, such as V_{DD} and GND lines.

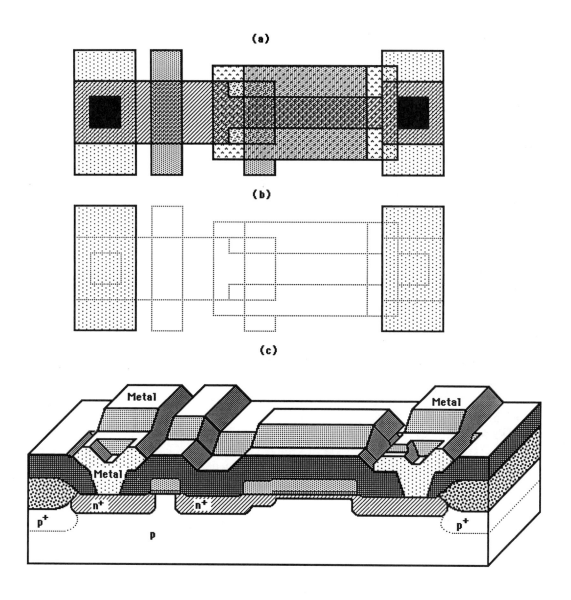

Figure 4-9: Metallization of the E-D inverter. Composite drawing of the layout (a), window in the mask (b), and cross-section (c).

4.2. IC elements in the NMOS technology

In this section we present details of transistors fabricated in NMOS technology. We begin with the devices forming an E-D inverter. Such an inverter is composed of two NMOS transistors: the **depletion transistor** connected in a current-source configuration that acts as an active **load**, and a **driver.** The driver is an **enhancement mode MOS transistor**, which is switched on or off by the input signal.

The details of the E-D inverter are shown in Fig. 4-10 (a) through (e). The depletion mode transistor, labeled T_2 connects the V_{DD} metal line (see Fig. 4-10 (a), (b), and (c)) and the inverter output, i.e. the region that is a source of T_2 and drain of T_1. Its gate is tied to the source through the buried contact (see Fig. 4-10 (b) and (c)) ($V_{GS}=0$).

The driver transistor, labeled T_1 has its source connected to the metal GND line, while its drain forms a diffusion region common with the source region of T_2. The input signal comes to the gate of the driver transistor (T_1), and the output signal is the voltage level in the output node, which connects the source and the gate of T_2 with the drain of T_1.

The aspect ratio, i.e. the width (W) to length (L)[*] ratio of both MOS transistors is directly readable from the layout shown in Fig. 4-10 (d) and (e).

---

[*]These transistor dimensions are usually labeled as W_{drawn} and L_{drawn}.

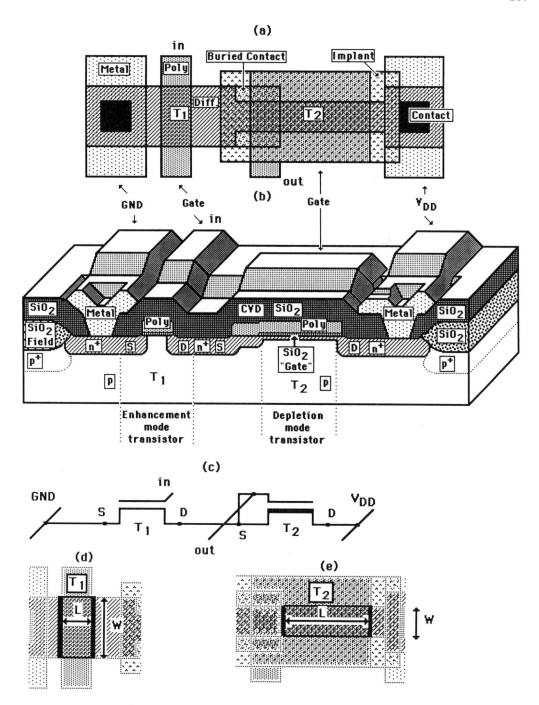

Figure 4-10: E-D inverter. Composite drawing of the layout (a), cross-section (b), the electrical diagram (c), the enhancement transistor (d), and the depletion transistor (e).

4.2.1. Enhancement transistor

The **n-channel enhancement transistor** is shown in Fig. 4-11.

The cross-section of this transistor is shown in Fig. 4-11 (b). Note that the effective or electrical channel length of this transistor L_{eff} equals the actual silicon gate length L reduced by the two lateral diffusion lengths. The length reduction results directly from the nature of the diffusion process (see Fig. 1-14). The depth of the lateral diffusion can be estimated as 0.8 of X_j. Note that modification of the actual channel length caused by lateral diffusion can be minimized if implantation is used rather than diffusion to create n^+ regions.

The dopant profile in Fig. 4-11 (d) exhibits a typical donor profile in shallow p-n^+ junctions. The concentration of acceptors in the channel is constant (Fig. 4-11 (c)). Since the channel is doped with acceptors, there are no electrons at all. As a result there is no conducting path between n^+ source and drain regions in zero-bias condition and therefore the enhancement type NMOS transistor is normally off.

The cross-section of the same transistor in the direction perpendicular to the current flow is shown in Fig. 4-11 (e). The effective channel width W_{eff} is smaller than the width of the active region. The phenomena that contribute to this difference are the lateral oxidation and lateral p^+ diffusion during the fabrication of the field oxide.

(a)

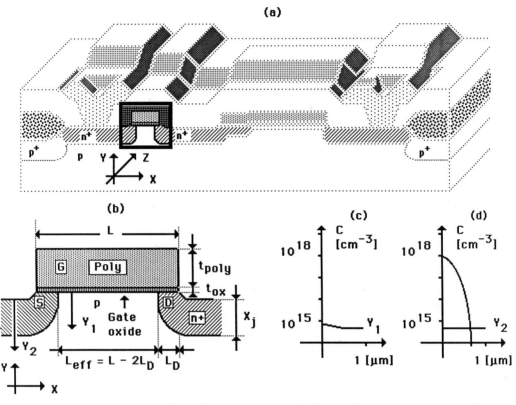

(b)

(c)

(d)

$L=3\mu m$, $X_j=0.6\mu m$, $L_D=0.8X_j=0.48\mu m$

$L_{eff}=2\mu m$, $t_{poly}=0.6\mu m$, $t_{ox}=0.05\mu m$

(e)

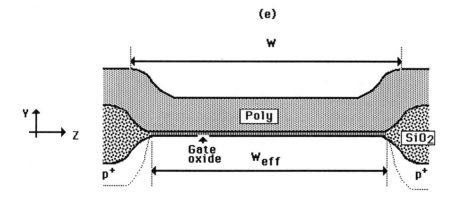

Figure 4-11: Enhancement transistor. The cross-section of the inverter with the enhancement transistor highlighted (a), cross-sections of the transistor (b) and (e), and impurity profiles in the channel (c) and drain (d) regions.

4.2.2. Depletion transistor

The second active device used in NMOS technology is the **n-channel depletion mode transistor,** shown in Fig. 4-12 (a).

It is again worth noting that the source of this transistor is extended by the n^+ region in the area of the buried contact. Thus the effective channel length L_{eff} equals the length of the polysilicon gate L reduced by the lateral diffusion length L_D and by the length of the buried contact L_{over}. The effective channel width W_{eff} is smaller than the appropriate mask dimension W.

The profile of impurities in n^+ source and drain regions (Fig. 4-12 (e)) is very similar to the profile in the enhancement transistor (Fig. 4-11 (d)), except for the smaller concentration level under the buried contact. But in the channel area the impurity profile is quite different (Fig. 4-12 (d)). The donor profile in the channel was created with the ion implantation process (see Fig. 4-4), and it enables the current flow between drain and source even when the gate voltage is zero. For this reason, a depletion NMOS transistor is normally on, in contrast to the enhancement type transistor.

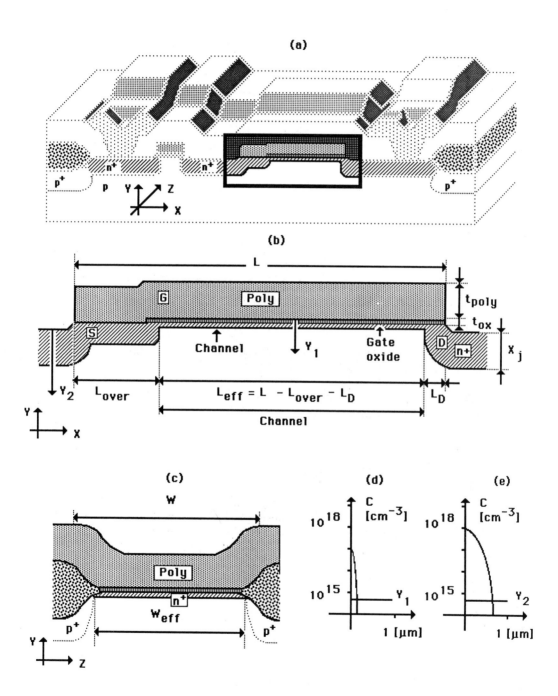

Figure 4-12:   Depletion transistor. The cross-section of the inverter
with the depletion transistor highlighted (a), cross-sections
of the transistor (b) and (c), and impurity profiles in the
channel (d), and buried contact and drain (e) regions.

4.2.3. Parasitic transistor

A structure where a metal line crosses two n^+ diffused regions forms a **parasitic transistor** (Fig. 4-13). If the voltage level of the metal line is high enough to induce a conducting path between two adjacent n^+ regions, the operation of the IC can be disturbed.

One of the advantages of the silicon gate NMOS process described in this chapter is that it minimizes the effect of parasitic MOS transistors. This is because

1. The field oxide fabricated using the local oxidation process (Fig. 1-6) can be made thick, and

2. The presence of a heavy p^+ doped region under the field oxide moves the threshold voltage of the parasitic transistor above the typical voltage range used in NMOS IC's.

Thus the parasitic transistors in NMOS circuits are off, and they are turned on only in the case of gross manufacturing errors.

(a)

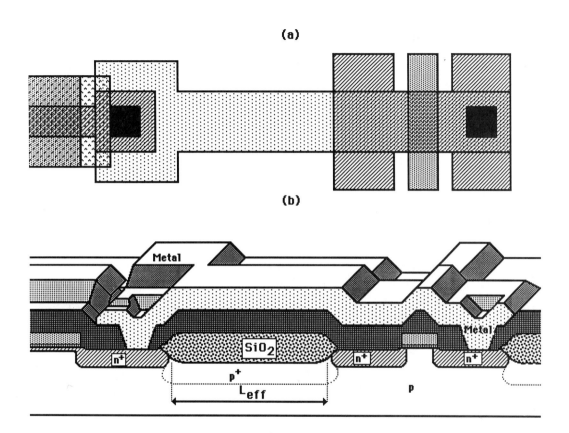

(b)

Figure 4-13: Parasitic transistor. Layout (a) and cross-section (b).

4.3. NMOS cells

A composite drawing of IC masks, i.e. an **IC layout**, contains all the information about IC transistors, connections, and parasitic elements. Nevertheless, an adequate interpretation of an IC layout is not an easy task. In this section we present a set of illustrations that may be used as an exercise in NMOS layout interpretation.

4.3.1. Cross-coupled NOR gates[*]

We begin with the electrical diagram of an RS flip-flop shown in Fig. 4-14. The layout of these **cross-coupled NOR gates** is presented in Fig. 4-15 through Fig. 4-20. Each lithography mask pattern is drawn on separate figures, shown with a black shaded area, with the remaining mask patterns in dotted lines. The final composite mask drawing is shown in Fig. 4-21.

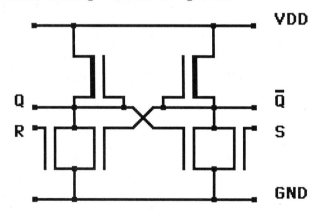

Figure 4-14:   Cross-coupled NOR gates (RS flip-flop).

---

[*]The masks shown in Fig. 4-15 through Fig. 4-21 have been extracted from the drawing presented in L. A. Glasser and D. W. Dobberpuhl, *The Design and Analysis of VLSI Circuits (Addison-Wesley Publishing Company, 1985)* on page 35.

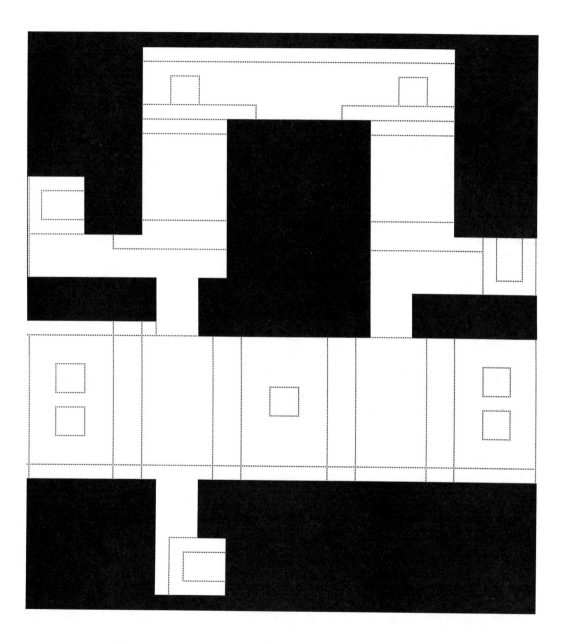

Figure 4-15: Active region mask of the cross-coupled NOR gates depicted in Fig. 4-14.

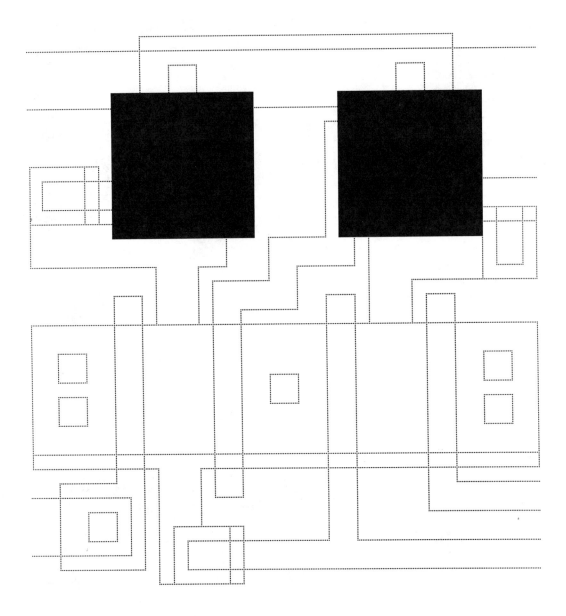

Figure 4-16: Depletion implant mask of the cross-coupled NOR gates
from Fig. 4-14.

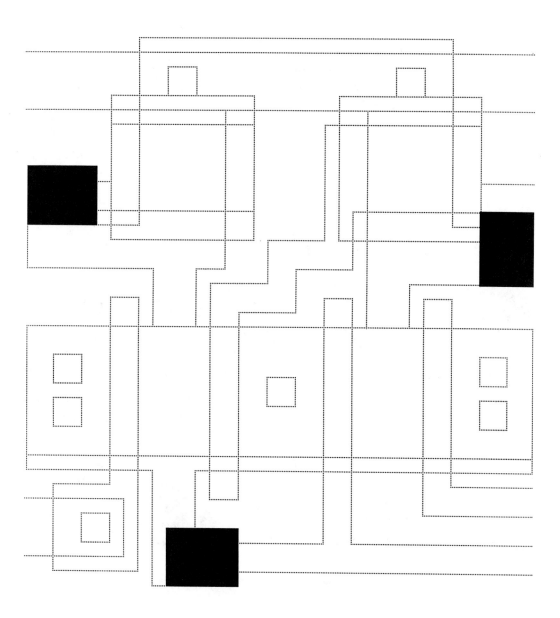

Figure 4-17: Buried contact mask of the cross-coupled NOR gates
from Fig. 4-14.

Figure 4-18: Polysilicon mask of the cross-coupled NOR gates
from Fig. 4-14.

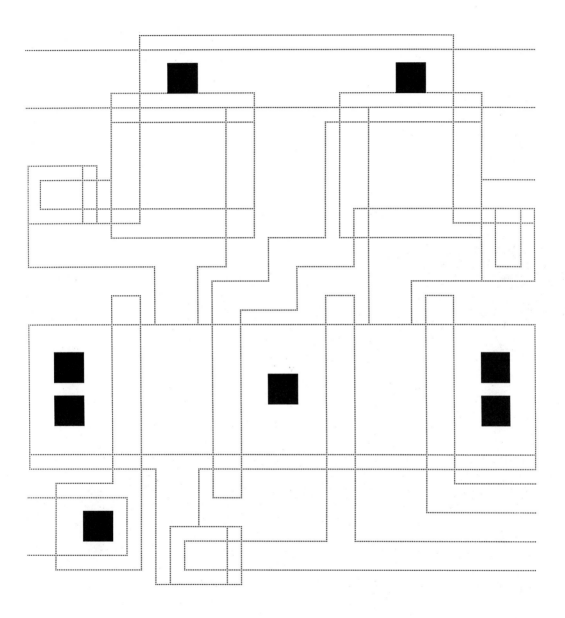

Figure 4-19: Contact cut mask of the cross-coupled NOR gates from Fig. 4-14.

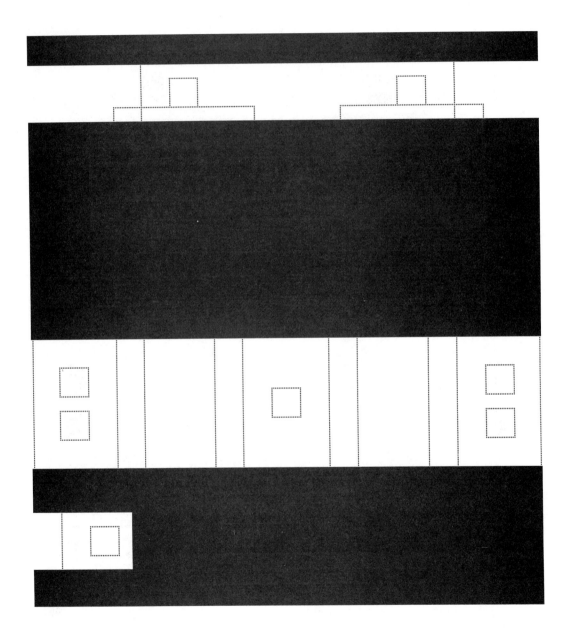

Figure 4-20: Metallization mask of the cross-coupled NOR gates
from Fig. 4-14.

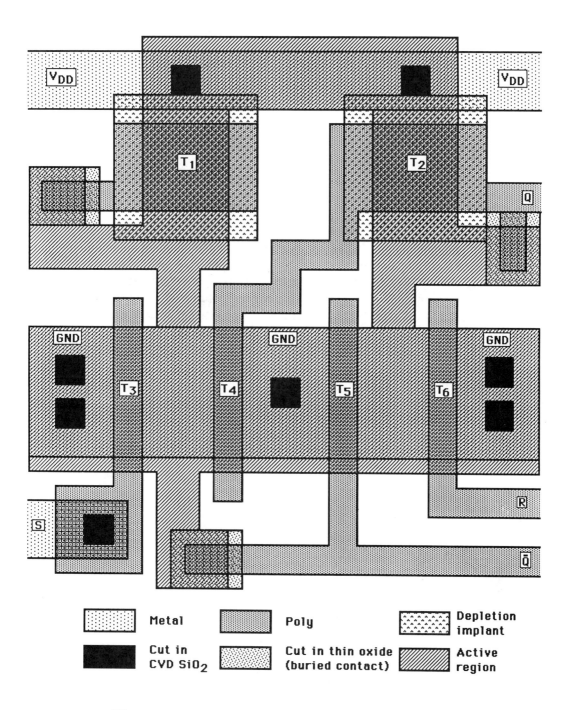

Figure 4-21: Composite drawing of the layout of the cross-coupled NOR gates from Fig. 4-14.

4.3.2. NOR gate

Using the E-D inverter, as discussed in Section 4.1, one can easily design the layout of other logic cells. For instance, if we replace the driver transistor in the E-D inverter with a couple of enhancement transistors connected in parallel and if we connect separate input signals to their gates, we will get a **NOR gate**. Two such enhancement transistors connected in parallel, with one common depletion transistor as a load, form a two-input NOR gate as shown in Fig. 4-22. Both the electrical circuit and the composite mask drawing of this gate are presented in Fig. 4-22 (a) and (b).

Note that in this design the location of the buried contact is different from that in the E-D inverter. The buried contact is now located far away from the channel of the depletion transistor. Thus the length of the depletion transistor channel is no longer sensitive to misalignment of the buried contact mask, as was the case for the inverter shown in Fig. 4-10.

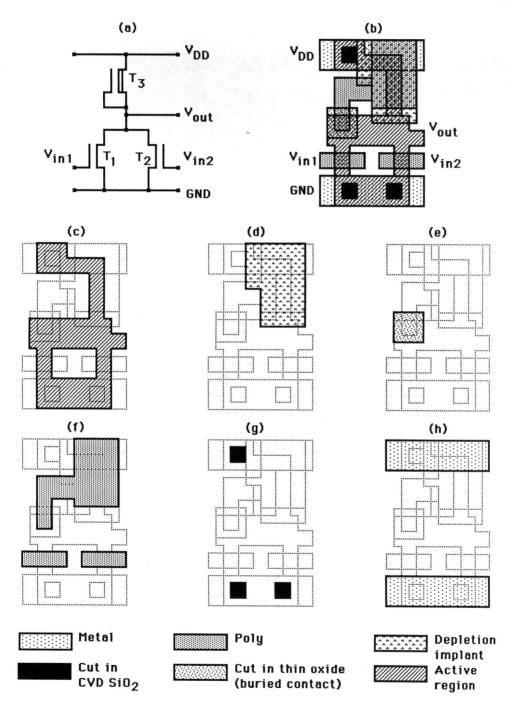

Figure 4-22:   An NMOS NOR gate. Electrical diagram (a), composite
layout (b), active region (c), implanted region (d), buried
contact (e), polysilicon (f), contact cuts (g), and
metallization (h).

An example of a **three-input NOR gate**, shown in Fig. 4-23, has three enhancement transistors connected in parallel between the output node and the ground. Although the presented design is similar to the previous gate, a couple of details are different. Three driver transistors have aspect ratios twice as big as those of the drivers in the two-input NOR. The load transistor is very similar, but the buried contact is again close to its channel. Moreover, the gate output node is connected to v_{out} using the same polysilicon line which forms the gate of the depletion transistor.

The whole layout presented in Fig. 4-23 is very compact and can be enclosed within a rectangle with most of its area occupied by gate elements. This design feature enables very close positioning of the basic cells forming a complex logic circuit and minimizes chip area.

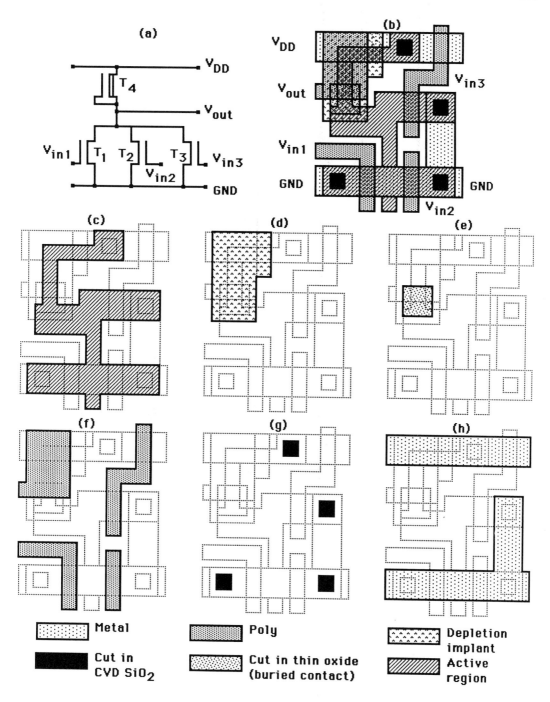

Figure 4-23: A three-input NMOS NOR gate. Electrical diagram (a), composite layout (b), active region (c), implanted region (d), buried contact (e), polysilicon (f), contact cuts (g), and metallization (h).

4.3.3. NAND gate

If we replace the driver transistor in the E-D inverter with a couple of enhancement transistors connected in series, the output signal will be a NAND function of input signals. The electric circuit and the composite mask drawing of such a **two-input NAND gate** are shown in Fig. 4-24 (a) and (b), and each of the drawings in Fig. 4-24 (c) to (h) presents the single photomask needed for fabrication of the cell.

In contrast to the NOR design, the electrical characteristics of the NAND gates in NMOS technology are very sensitive to the number of input transistors. As each enhancement transistor represents some non-zero resistance when switched on, too many transistors in series could degrade the output node low voltage level, and in consequence would change the output logic state. To eliminate this effect, NAND gates usually have no more than three inputs.

Note that most of the design is similar to the gate presented in Fig. 4-22, but that some details are new. The new feature of the gate output node is that there are two separate terminals. The first goes to the left side of the gate and is an n^+ diffusion region. The second terminal goes to the right side and is an n^+-doped polysilicon region.

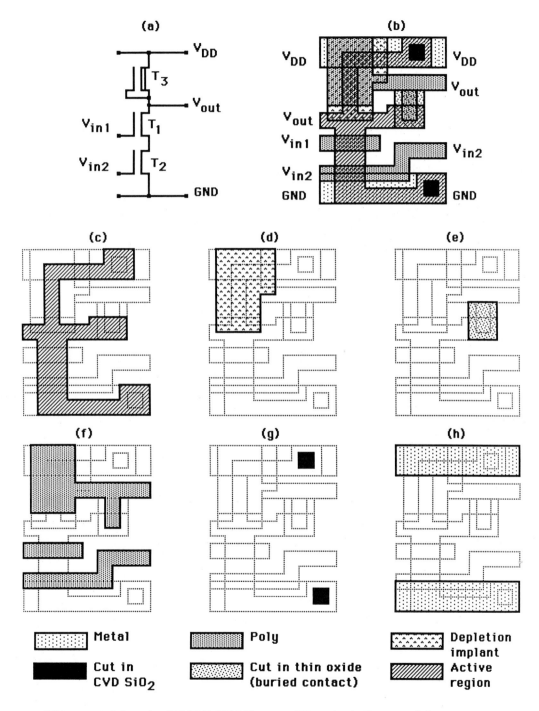

Figure 4-24: An NMOS NAND gate. Electrical diagram (a), composite layout (b), active region (c), implanted region (d), buried contact (e), polysilicon (f), contact cuts (g), and metallization (h).

4.3.4. AND-OR-INVERT gate

A more complex design is an **AND-OR-INVERT gate,** which is shown in Fig. 4-25. Instead of one driver transistor it contains three enhancement type transistors: T_2 connected in series with T_3, and both of them connected in parallel with T_1. This combination of driver transistors connected with a depletion transistor T_4 as a load forms an AND-OR-INVERT gate.

Both the electric circuit and the layout of this gate are shown in Fig. 4-25 (a) and (b), and the subsequent mask patterns are highlighted in Fig. 4-25 (c) through (h).

The AND-OR-INVERT gate is constrained by the same limitations as the NAND gate: the number of driver transistors connected in series in one branch should not exceed three. However, the number of branches connected in parallel is theoretically unlimited, as was the case for the NOR gate. But as the number of branches grows, the area of the output diffusion node increases, thus increasing the parasitic capacitance of the output node (see Section 4.3.7). Since this can degrade the circuit speed, the practical limit for the number of "OR"-connected branches is a compromise between circuit speed and complexity of the design.

It is typical for the AND-OR-INVERT gate design that the dimensions of the driver transistors are different, because the equivalent conductance (or equivalent aspect ratio) of each of the OR-connected branches should be the same. This explains why the transistors T_2 and T_3 are twice as wide as the transistor T_1.

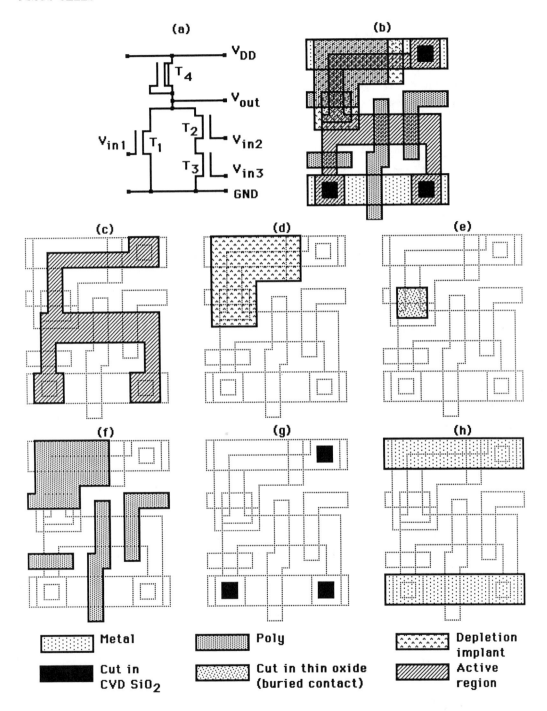

Figure 4-25: An NMOS AND-OR-INVERT gate. Electrical diagram (a), composite layout (b), active region (c), implanted region (d), buried contact (e), polysilicon (f), contact cuts (g), and metallization (h).

4.3.5. Various devices in the NOR gate

An IC layout can be seen as a collection of masks and also as a collection of devices. In previous examples we presented a mask-oriented interpretation of the circuit layout. In this section we interpret the layout of the NOR gate introduced in Section 4.3.2 as a collection of devices.

Three transistors — or more exactly, their channels — are shown in Fig. 4-26 (c). The enhancement transistor is determined as a common part of the active region and the polysilicon region. The depletion transistor region is an intersection of the active region, polysilicon mask, and depletion implant region.

Drain and source regions are shown in Fig. 4-26 (d). These regions exhibit parasitic resistances and the parasitic capacitance of the flat part of the p-n junction.

Part of the polysilicon which is outside the active region represents parasitic capacitances connected between the polysilicon and the p^+ substrate (Fig. 4-26 (e)).

Part of the metal layer which is outside the active region (Fig. 4-26 (f)) forms parasitic capacitances connected between the polysilicon and the p^+ substrate.

The metal layer on top of the polysilicon (Fig. 4-26 (g)) forms parasitic capacitances $C_{Al\text{-}polysilicon}$, which sometimes are large enough to cause feedback between metal and polysilicon lines.

The metal lines that overlap the n^+ diffusion region are the parasitic capacitances $C_{Al\text{-}n^+}$, shown in Fig. 4-26 (h).

The regions in Fig. 4-26 (i) exhibit the parasitic capacitances of the cylindrical and spherical parts of the p-n junction. They are connected in parallel with the junction capacitance depicted in Fig. 4-26 (d). They are presented as devices of a separate category because they are formed on the junction of the n^+ region and the heavily doped channel-stop p^+ region. Thus, they are larger than capacitances formed on the n^+ and substrate junction.

The last important elements, shown in Fig. 4-26 (j), represent gate-source and gate-drain overlap capacitances (see also Fig. 4-28). Despite their small sizes they are important because they cause an output-input feedback and therefore strongly affect the circuit performance.

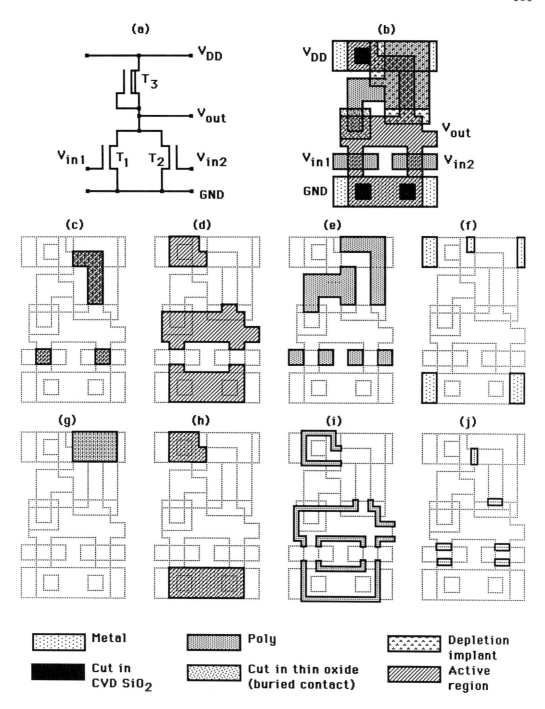

Figure 4-26:   Elements of the NOR gate.

4.3.6. Cross-sections of NMOS IC's

Full understanding of the manufacturing process and the circuit layout allow seeing a 2-D layout as a 3-D structure. The 3-D interpretation of the IC layout can in some cases be more complex than we would expect. To illustrate this fact in this section we present a couple of cross-sections of the three-input NOR gate introduced in Section 4.3.2.

The drawing in Fig. 4-27 (b) is a circuit cross-section along the A line. We can clearly see two enhancement MOS transistors connected to the common output diffusion node and two Al-n$^+$ contacts, which short sources of the transistors to the ground. Fig. 4-27 (c) presents a circuit cross-section along the B line. This intersection line cuts the polysilicon-n$^+$ buried contact and the third enhancement MOS transistor.

The last cross-section (Fig. 4-27 (d)) cuts the NOR gate along the C line. Going from the right to the left side of Fig. 4-27 (d) we can see several other circuit elements, such as the double parasitic capacitance ($C_{Al\text{-}polysilicon}$ and $C_{polysilicon\text{-}sub}$), the depletion MOS transistor with the buried channel intersection, the parasitic capacitance between the poly line and the substrate, and the contact Al-n$^+$.

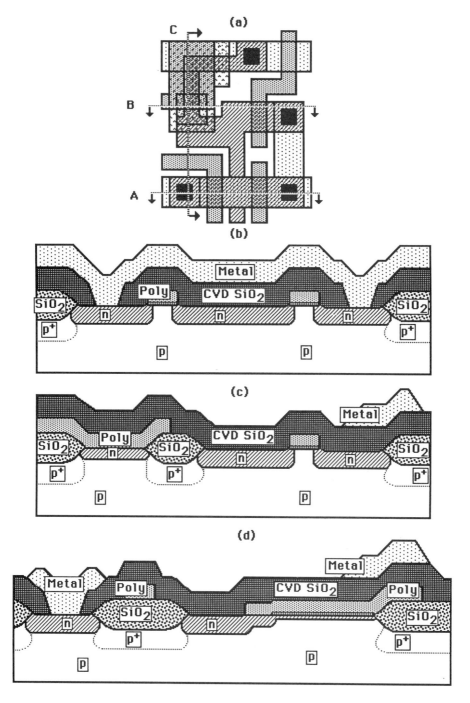

Figure 4-27: Cross-sections of the three-input NOR gate. Composite layout (a), and circuit cross-sections along the A, B, C lines (b) - (d).

4.3.7. Parasitic capacitances in the NMOS gate

In the analysis of the NMOS gate it is essential to determine which of the parasitic devices may affect the performance of the gate. It is important because some of the gate elements do not affect the performance while others do. To illustrate this point we show in Fig. 4-28 a segment of the circuit and we analyze regions in the layout that do switch their potential between GND and V_{DD}. In Fig. 4-28 (a) and (b) the electrical diagram and the composite layout of this circuit are shown.

In Fig. 4-28 (c), (d), and (e) the potential distributions for various combinations of input signals are depicted. By comparing these three drawings we find that in the analyzed circuit some regions do not change their potentials. Fig. 4-28 (f) indicates regions which do switch their potentials. Note that capacitances connected to these regions have to be charged or discharged while all other regions will preserve their voltages and thus charges. Thus the essential capacitances are those associated with regions surrounded by a bold line in Fig. 4-28 (f). They are both MOS transistor gate capacitances and parasitic capacitances associated with the n^+-substrate junction and polysilicon lines over the thick oxide.

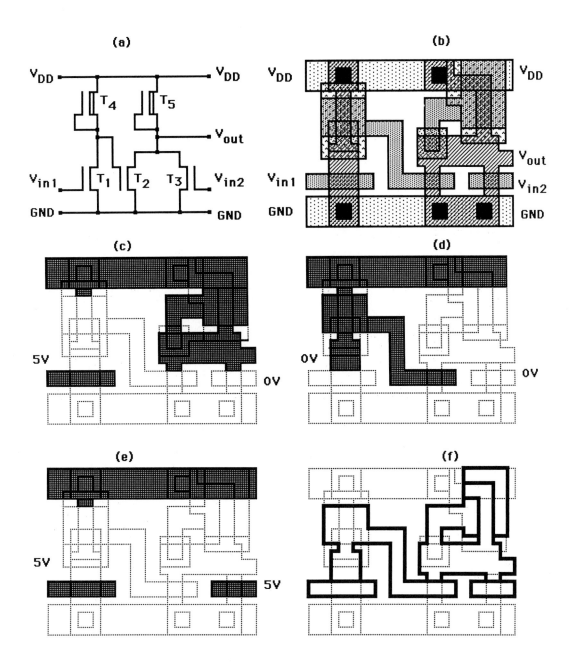

Figure 4-28:   Parasitic capacitances in the NMOS gate. Electrical diagram
(a), composite layout (b), constant voltage regions for various
input signals (c) - (e), and switching capacitances (f).

Chapter 5
CMOS Technology

with contributions from
Andrzej J. Strojwas

Complementary MOS (CMOS) technology, which provides both n-channel and p-channel MOS transistors on one chip, is becoming the dominant candidate for VLSI applications.

CMOS technologies can be divided into two main categories:

- **bulk technologies**, in which IC's are fabricated in silicon substrate wafers, and

- **silicon on insulator (SOI) technologies**, in which IC's are created in a thin layer of single-crystal silicon which is grown on an insulator such as sapphire.

In this book we will discuss technologies of both categories. This chapter begins with one of the simplest versions of bulk technology.

To accommodate both NMOS and PMOS transistors on one chip, special regions must be created in which the semiconductor type is opposite to the substrate type. These regions are called **wells** or **tubs**. Two types of wells exist. A p-well is created in an n-type substrate, and an n-well is created in a p-type substrate wafer. Of course, an NMOS transistor is defined in the p-type substrate, and a PMOS transistor is created in the n-type substrate. There is also the possibility of creating both an n-well and a p-well in a low-concentration substrate material. The latter is called a **twin-tub process**. In this chapter we describe n-well technology.

In the next section, a sequence of the most important steps in a simple n-well fabrication process is presented. The process under study defines a static CMOS inverter. To simplify the description, field implantation steps and threshold adjust channel implants have been left out. Each step is presented by a top view of the lithographic masks (if lithography is performed) and a cross-sectional view.

5.1. N-well CMOS technology

The n-well fabrication process starts with a moderately doped (typically less than 10^{15}cm^{-3}) p-type substrate (wafer). Then an initial oxide (**barrier oxide**) layer is grown on the entire surface. The first lithographic mask, shown in Fig. 5-1, defines the n-well region. N-type impurity atoms, usually phosphorus, are implanted through the window in the oxide. However, since we are not able to implant the impurity atoms deep enough, the impurities have to be driven-in (or redistributed) in the next high-temperature operation. Note that this redistribution occurs not only in the vertical direction but also laterally, thus increasing the transistor size and limiting the density of the devices on the chip. The surface concentration is typically around 10^{16}cm^{-3}, and due to the long, high-temperature redistribution process the gradient of the impurity concentration is typically rather small. In other words, the well impurity profile is relatively flat.

(a)

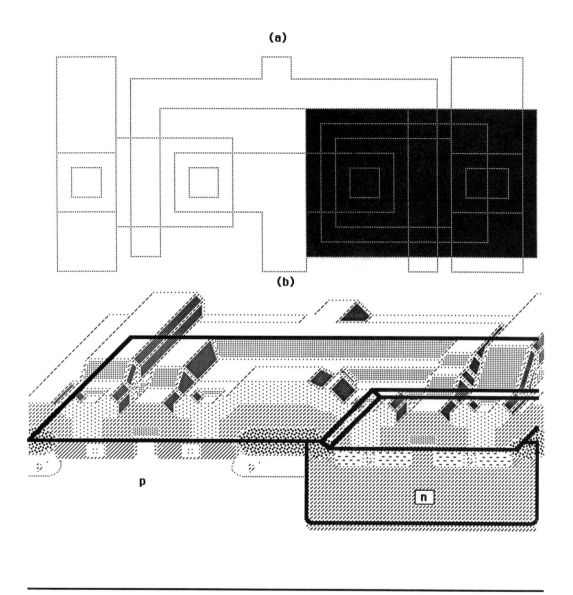

(b)

Figure 5-1: Well implant and drive-in in the n-well CMOS inverter. Window in the mask (a) and cross-section (b).

After well implant and drive-in the next sequence of steps is performed to define the active regions in which MOS transistors will be created. The formation of active regions illustrated in Fig. 5-2 and Fig. 5-3 is accomplished through local oxidation of silicon (the so-called **semi-recessed LOCOS process**). In this process thick regions of silicon dioxide are selectively grown on the silicon substrate to provide isolation between NMOS and PMOS transistors. This thick oxide is typically called a **field oxide** (FOX). Transistors will be defined later in regions without FOX.

To protect the silicon surface from oxidation, a silicon nitride (Si_3N_4) layer is used. In order to minimize the stress between the nitride layer and the silicon substrate a thin **pad oxide** layer is grown. The nitride layer is deposited on the pad oxide and then selectively etched in such a way that only the active regions are protected by the nitride (see the active region mask and resulting nitride region in Fig. 5-2).

After nitride etching a channel-stop boron implant is performed. This implant has a dose and energy large enough to increase the concentration of acceptors of the p regions outside the active region, but it cannot change the type of the n-well. Thus the silicon surface that is not covered by the nitride and is not in the well has a significantly increased concentration of acceptors (see Fig. 5-2 (b)).

(a)

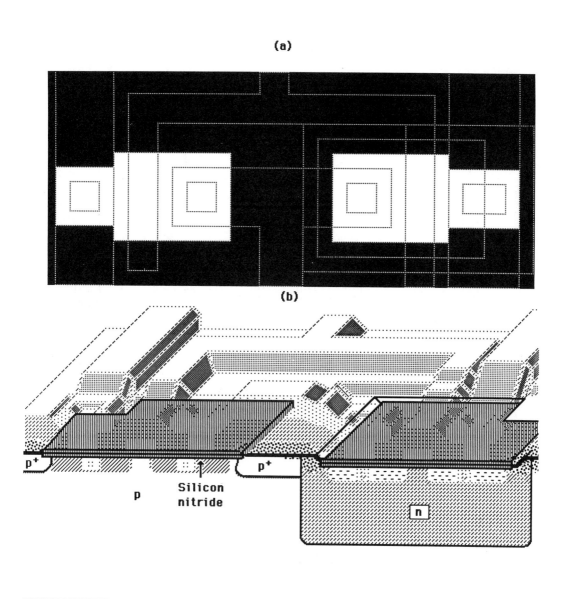

(b)

Figure 5-2: Formation of the active regions in the n-well CMOS inverter.
Window in the mask (a) and cross-section of the inverter (b).

Next the silicon wafer is oxidized using a long, high-temperature cycle. A thick oxide layer (up to 1 micron) is grown in the regions unprotected by silicon nitride. Since in the thermal oxide growth silicon atoms are consumed, the resulting structure becomes non-planar. Moreover, due to the lateral diffusion of oxidant under the nitride layer, the oxidation process is two-dimensional and the so-called "bird's beak" regions are created. Edges of field oxide with the bird's beak are shown in Fig. 5-3 (a) and (b). The lateral penetration of bird's beak regions can be comparable to the vertical field oxide thickness. In this step, the n-well region impurities are driven-in slightly deeper. It should be noted, however, that this is in practice the last really significant thermal step that has a strong effect on the impurity distribution.

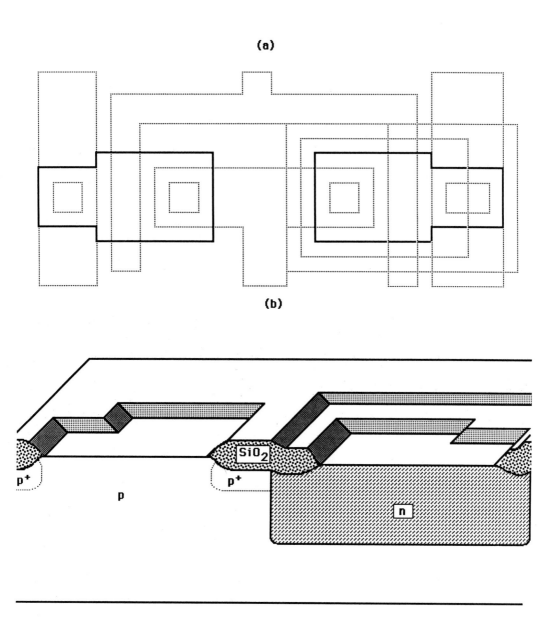

Figure 5-3: Active regions in the n-well CMOS inverter.
Edges of active regions in the mask (a) and cross-section
of the inverter (b).

In the next step the layer of Si_3N_4 is removed by an etchant that does not affect the oxide, and then the thin pad oxide layer is removed. Now a thin gate oxide layer (typically less than 0.3 μm) is grown thermally in the furnace. The gate oxide has to be of the highest quality because it will strongly affect the threshold voltage of the MOS transistors. Of course, the gate oxide is grown only in the open area of the active region (Fig. 5-4 (a)). The effect of gate oxidation on the field oxide is practically negligible.

(a)

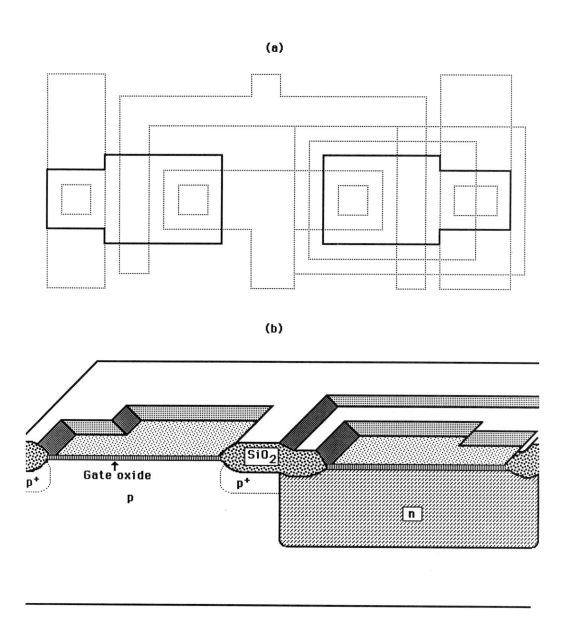

(b)

Figure 5-4: Gate oxide growth in the n-well CMOS inverter.
Edges of the gate oxide regions (a) and cross-section of the
inverter (b).

In the next step the polysilicon layer is deposited over the entire wafer. The chemical vapor deposition (CVD) process is used for this purpose. The polysilicon is doped during the deposition. Typically the polysilicon is doped with phosphorus (n-type impurity). In more complicated CMOS processes, polysilicon is chemically doped to obtain a higher concentration of phosphorus and thus lower resistivity. Resistivity is an important parameter of the poly layer since polysilicon is used not only as a gate material ut also for interconnections. Note also that control of the impurity vconcentration in polysilicon is important because the work function, which affects the threshold voltage, is a function of the impurity concentration in the poly layer.

Using the mask shown in Fig. 5-5 (a), undesired poly is removed in the dry (plasma) etching process and thus the gate regions and the interconnect patterns are defined. The accuracy of this lithography step (including plasma etching) is of crucial importance because in this self-aligned technology poly serves as a mask for the source/drain implantation. Therefore, variations in the poly line width will result in variations of the transistor channel length which will, in turn, strongly affect transistor performance.

After polysilicon etching the thin gate oxide is etched and the resulting structures with clearly defined transistors are formed (see Fig. 5-5).

(a)

(b)

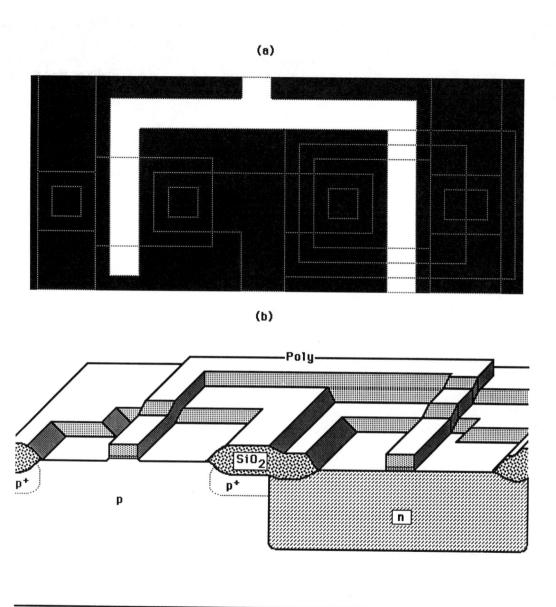

Figure 5-5: Polysilicon region in the n-well CMOS inverter. Window in the mask (a) and cross-section of the inverter (b).

An n^+ mask (Fig. 5-6 (a)) is then used for implantation of arsenic atoms to define the source and drain regions of NMOS transistors. Simultaneously, an ohmic contact to the n-well is formed. This mask is often called an **n-select mask**. Arsenic is preferred over phosphorus to obtain shallow junctions and minimal lateral diffusion. High doses of arsenic have to be used in order to achieve low-resistance source/drain regions (used as local interconnects) and good ohmic contacts. The typical values of source/drain sheet resistance should be below 30 Ω per square.

(a)

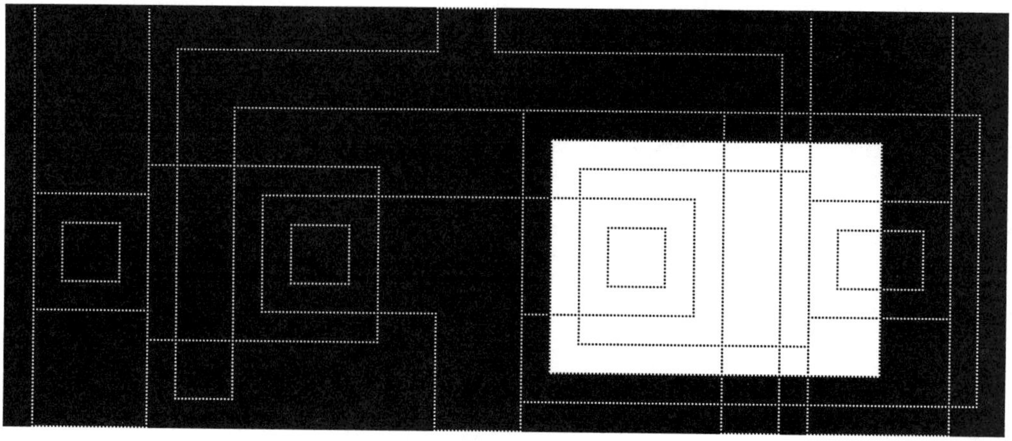

(b)

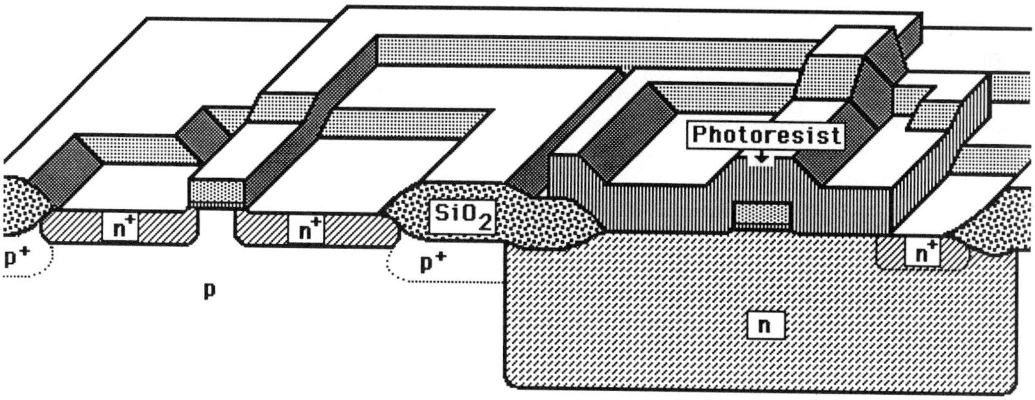

Figure 5-6: Implantation of n-channel transistor drain and source. Window in the n-select mask (a) and cross-section of the inverter (b).

In the following step a negative (or complement) of the n-select mask is used to define the p^+ source/drain regions of PMOS transistors and the ohmic contacts to the substrate (Fig. 5-7). Boron is used as the dopant in the process step. Again, the polysilicon layer protects transistor channel regions from the boron dopant.

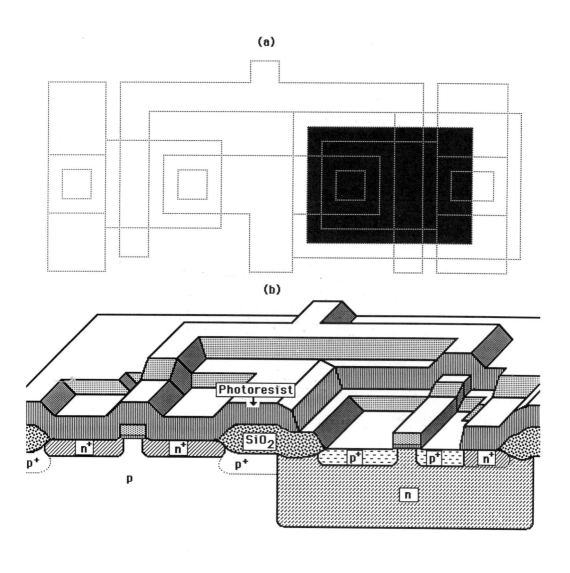

Figure 5-7: Implantation of p$^+$ regions.
Window in the negative of the n-select mask (a)
and cross-section of the inverter (b).

The sequence of implantations described above forms two p^+ regions and an n^+ region in the n-well (see Fig. 5-8). Note that the boundary between these regions is located in the center of the contact window (dotted line in the cross-section).

After implantation of the source/drain regions a rather short thermal process at moderate temperature is performed to drive the impurities deeper into the silicon substrate. This process is often called source/drain annealing. The goal here is to repair some of the crystal structure damage that occurred in the high-dose implantation without a significant lateral diffusion of the source/drain regions under the gate (such lateral diffusion would cause undesired gate-to-source and gate-to-drain overlap capacitances).

(a)

(b)

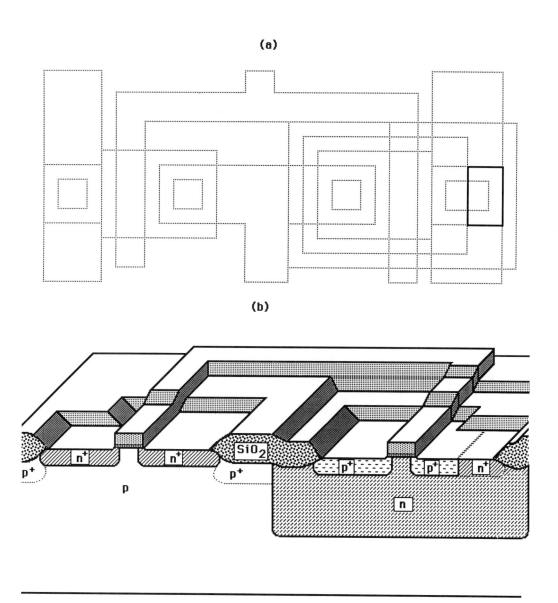

Figure 5-8: N^+ region in the n-well of the CMOS inverter.
Edges of the drain region of the p-channel device and
the n^+ region in the n-well (a) and cross-section of the
inverter (b).

Next the SiO_2 insulating layer is deposited over the entire wafer area using a CVD technique (Fig. 5-9). Note the nonplanarity of the surface that will have an impact on the metal deposition step.

(a)

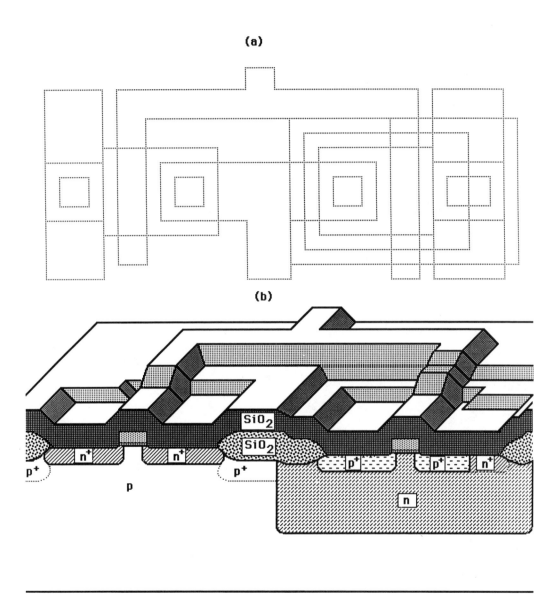

(b)

Figure 5-9:   CVD deposition of SiO$_2$ in the n-well CMOS process.
Layout (a) and cross-section of the inverter (b).

In the next step another lithographic mask (Fig. 5-10 (a)) is used to define contact cuts in the insulating layer. The goal is to expose either bare silicon in the source/drain areas or the polysilicon layer (not shown here). Contacts to polysilicon must be made outside the gate regions to avoid metal spikes through the poly and the thin gate oxide.

(a)

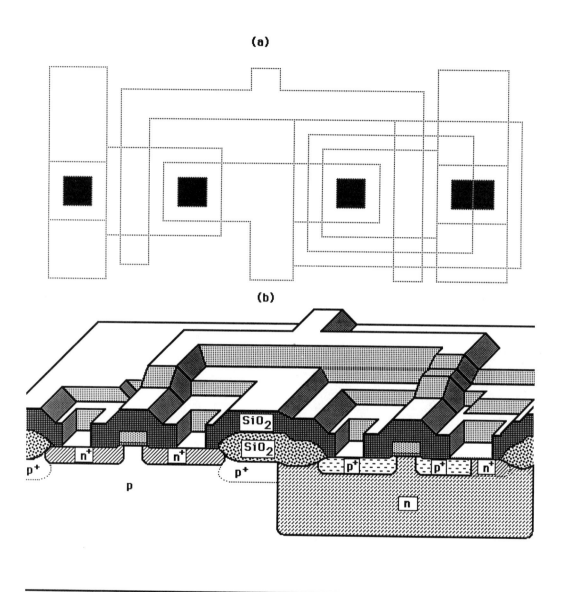

(b)

Figure 5-10: Contact cuts in the n-well CMOS inverter. Window in the mask (a) and cross-section of the inverter (b).

Next aluminum (Al) is deposited over the entire wafer using the evaporation process. The step coverage in this process is most critical because of the non-planarity of the wafer surface. This can lead to breaks in the metal paths which can be either created during the fabrication process or can be caused later on by electromigration phenomena. The metallization mask defines the interconnection pattern (in our case connections between the drains of PMOS and NMOS transistors and the V_{DD} and GND rails, shown in Fig. 5-11 (a) and (b)). Undesired metal is removed in the etching step.

(a)

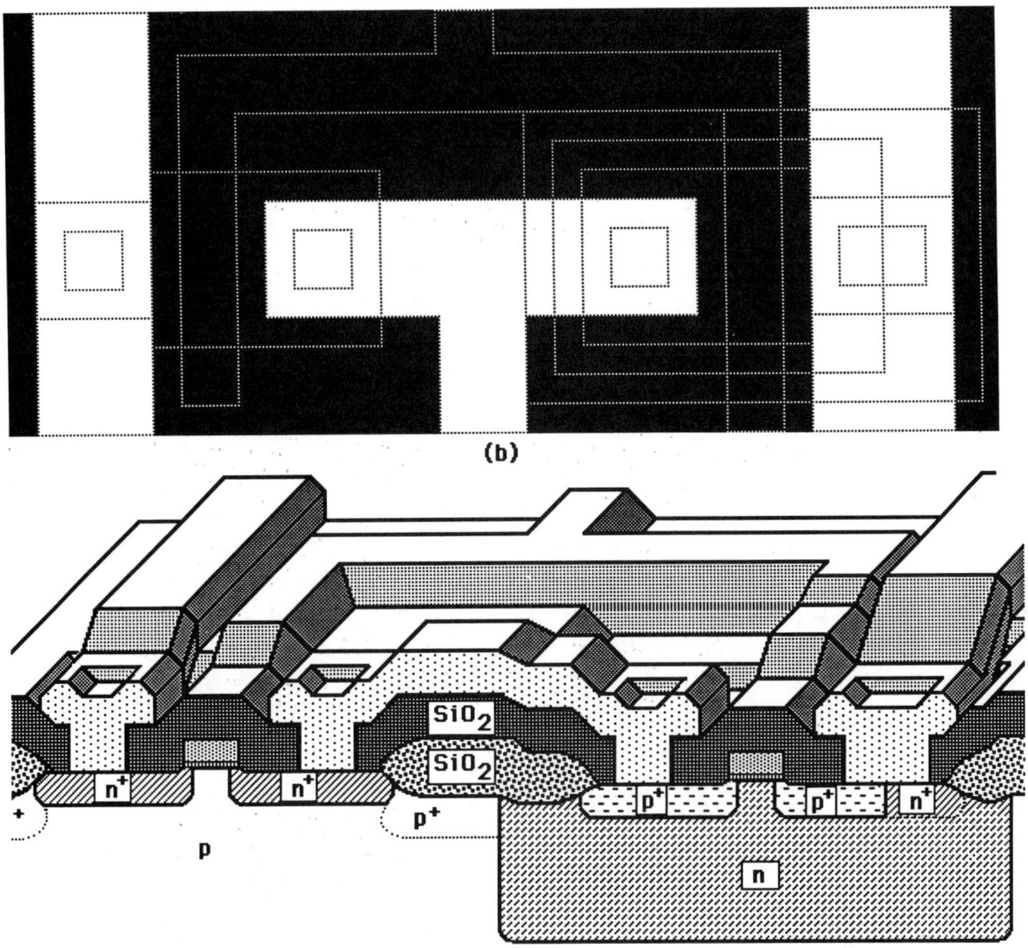

(b)

Figure 5-11: Metallization in the n-well CMOS inverter. Window in the mask (a) and cross-section of the inverter (b).

In the final step of the wafer fabrication the entire surface is **passivated** (overglass layer, not shown here) to protect the surface from contaminants and scratches. Then openings are etched to the bond pads to allow for wire bonding. Of course, this requires another lithographic mask which is not shown in the Figure.

The composite layout and the resulting cross-sectional view, and the electrical diagram of the CMOS inverter implemented in the n-well technology described above are shown in Fig. 5-12. Note that in this particular drawing as in the previous drawings connections between the GND line and the substrate of n-channel transistors are not shown. In the actual circuit such connections exist and are created in the form of a contact similar to the contact between the V_{DD} line and the n-well, shown in Fig. 5-12 (b), or as a separate contact common for several different cells.

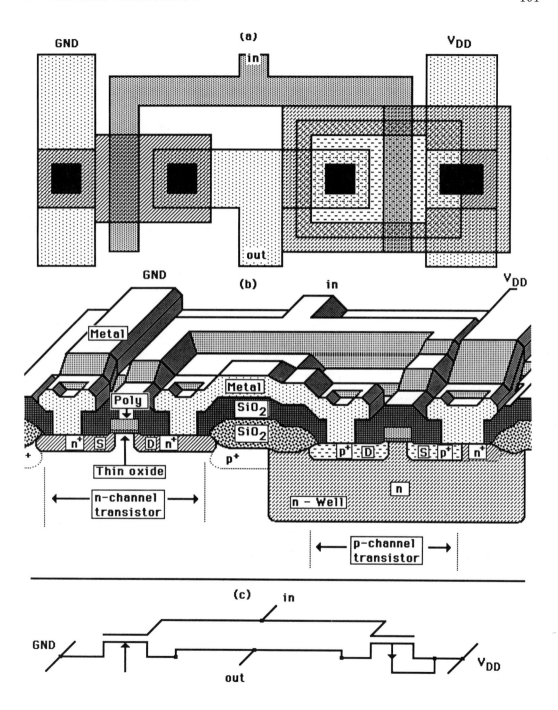

Figure 5-12: CMOS inverter. Composite layout (a),
cross-section (b), and electrical diagram (c).

5.2. Layout of the NAND gate[*]

The purpose of this section is to demonstrate a layout design style for simple CMOS gates. We use the static two-input NAND gate as an example of layout design. The circuit diagram of this gate is shown in Fig. 5-13. Fig. 5-14 shows the composite layout of this NAND gate. Note that the layout is not a direct translation of the gate diagram. The NMOS and PMOS transistors (i.e. the active regions) are oriented horizontally while the polysilicon gates run vertically. Such an arrangement allows for high density and regularity in the multiple-input static CMOS gates. Moreover, the capacitance of the drain-substrate junctions is minimized in this configuration. To minimize the gate area, one of the polysilicon lines has a jog. Fig. 5-15 through Fig. 5-21 show the lithographic masks necessary to implement this gate in the n-well CMOS process described in the previous section. Note that in order to reduce the susceptibility to latch-up, the n-well is connected to V_{DD} and the substrate is grounded. To assure good ohmic contacts, regions under the contact are subjected to source/drain implantations.

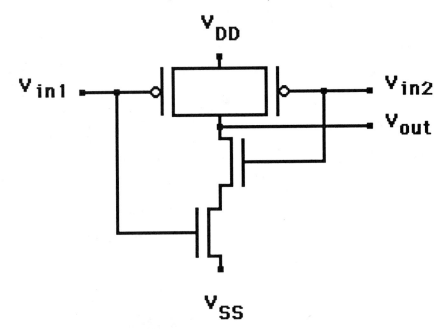

Figure 5-13: Circuit diagram of the two-input CMOS NAND gate

---

[*]Main elements of the masks shown in Fig. 5-15 through Fig. 5-21 have been extracted from the drawing presented in N.Weste and K.Eshraghian, *Principles of CMOS VLSI Design - A System Perspective (Addison-Wesley Publishing Company, 1985)* on Plate 4.

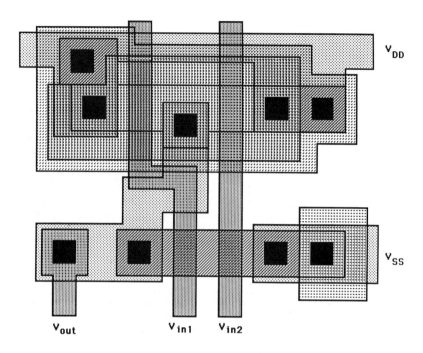

Figure 5-14:   Composite layout of the CMOS NAND gate

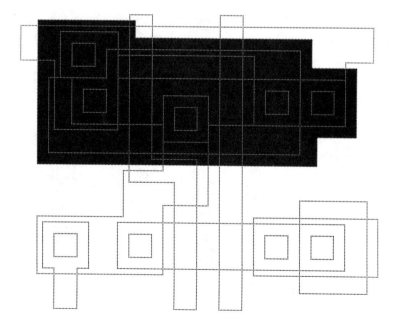

Figure 5-15:   Well implant in the n-well CMOS NAND gate.

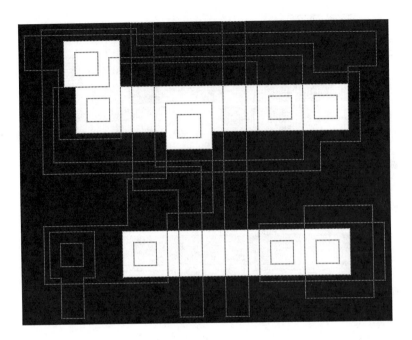

Figure 5-16: Active regions in the n-well CMOS NAND gate.

Figure 5-17: Polysilicon regions in the n-well CMOS NAND gate.

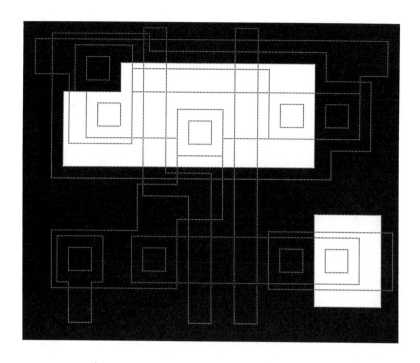

Figure 5-18: N^+ regions implantation in the n-well CMOS NAND gate.

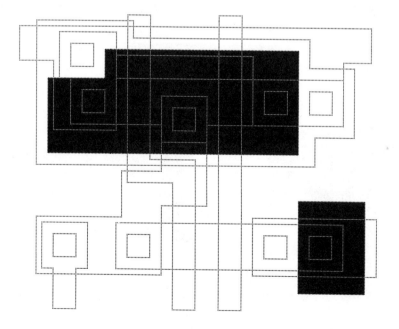

Figure 5-19: P^+ regions implantation in the n-well CMOS NAND gate.

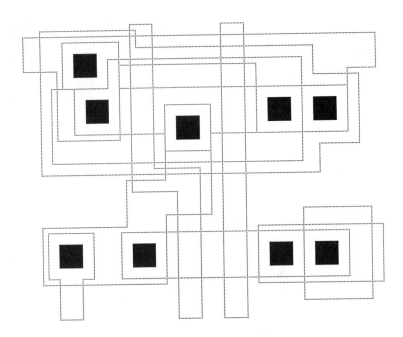

Figure 5-20:   Contact cuts in the n-well CMOS NAND gate.

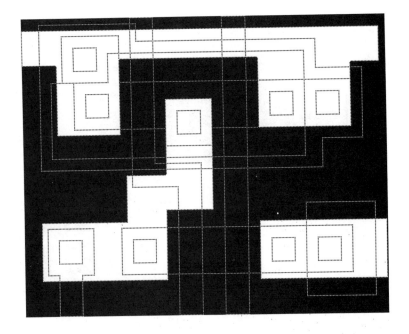

Figure 5-21:   Metallization of the n-well CMOS NAND gate.

Chapter 6
Advanced   Bipolar Technology

The bipolar technology presented in Chapter 3 is the oldest of all IC technologies. The NMOS and CMOS technologies were developed much later and they were supposed to supplement the traditional bipolar process. In the mid-1970s, it was hoped that the new generation of NMOS and CMOS processes would eventually replace the bipolar process entirely.

Ten years later the reality is different, however. The bipolar process still dominates high-speed memory and logic. There are also some indications that bipolar circuits may regain some areas of applications that have been dominated by MOS processes since the late 1970s.

The purpose of this chapter is to illustrate some of the concepts that have been used to upgrade the traditional bipolar process so that this more than twenty-year-old technology can compete with the much younger MOS processes.

6.1. Inherent limitations in the traditional bipolar technologies

Traditional bipolar technology uses p-n junctions to isolate different IC components. As was shown in Chapter 3, these junctions are created using diffusion. To create effective insulation, a p-type dopant has to be diffused all the way through the epitaxial layer. Since lateral diffusion is comparable to vertical diffusion, the lateral diffusion of the isolation must be comparable to the thickness of the epitaxial layer (Fig. 6-1). In addition, the lateral dimension of the insulation includes the depletion region associated with the p-n junction. Consequently, the minimal spacing between the edge of the base diffusion and the edge of the insulation must be large and the silicon area occupied by the active devices is small compared to the area occupied by the insulation (Fig. 6-1).

The other disadvantage of traditional bipolar technology is caused by parasitic capacitors formed by island-isolation junctions. These capacitances usually store a lot of collector charge and therefore affect the circuit's speed.

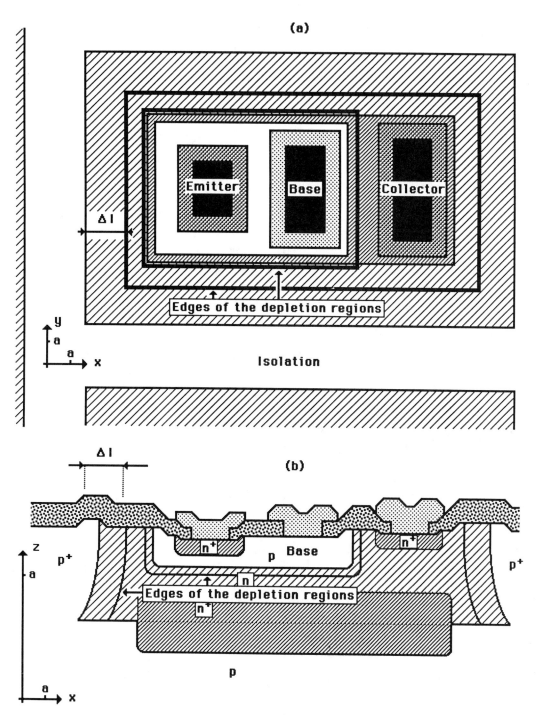

Figure 6-1: Minimal distances between edges of various regions in the npn transistor fabricated with the traditional bipolar technology.

6.2. Bipolar technology with oxide isolation

The main concept in the technology described in this section is the application of a silicon dioxide isolation instead of a junction isolation. This concept allows for a drastic decrease in the device size and thus results in an increase in both density and speed of bipolar IC's.

6.2.1. Technology

The bipolar technology with the oxide isolation uses lightly doped p-type substrate with $<111>$, or in the newer processes with $<100>$, orientation.

In the first processing step the silicon substrate is oxidized (Fig. 6-2 (a)). Then, using a buried layer mask (Fig. 6-2 (b)), windows are etched in the SiO_2 (Fig. 6-2 (b)) and arsenic or antimony dopant is used to implant buried layer regions (Fig. 6-2 (c)). As in traditional bipolar technology, these heavily doped n^+ regions are used to minimize resistance between the collector contact and the C-B junction.

After buried layer implantation, a long, high-temperature drive-in step pushes dopants deeper into the substrate (Fig. 6-2 (d)). The drive-in is performed in an oxidizing atmosphere so that a layer of SiO_2 is grown on the surface of the wafer. Note that the oxidation rate in the window is different from that in the region covered with previously grown oxide (Fig. 6-2 (d)), so when the SiO_2 is stripped off edges of the buried layers can be seen on the surface of the wafer (Fig. 6-2 (e)).

In the next processing step an epitaxial layer is grown (Fig. 6-2 (f)). This high-temperature step is very crucial because the eventual quality of the IC devices depends on the quality of the epitaxial layer. Of special concern are various defects that may be introduced into the crystalline structure of the epitaxial layer. The epitaxial layer is chemically doped with n-type dopant during the layer growth. Dopant concentration in the layer is uniform and low. The epitaxial layer is also doped by diffusion from the n^+ regions, but this process is slow because arsenic or antimony have very low diffusion coefficients.

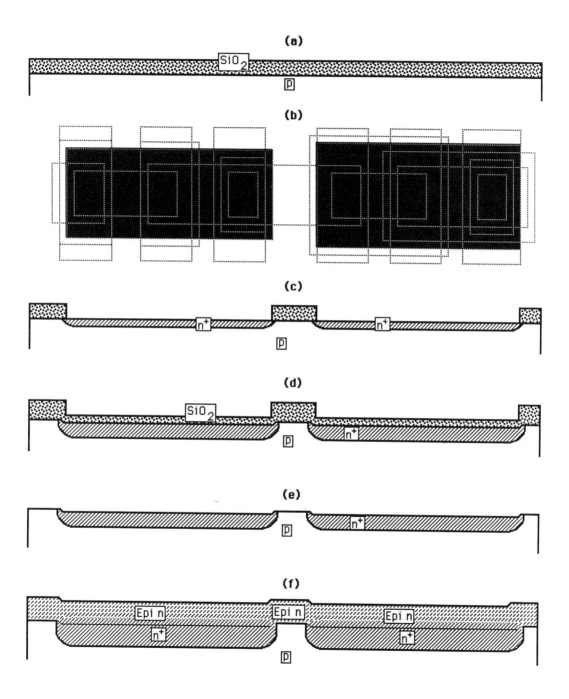

Figure 6-2: Advanced bipolar process. Part I.

The goal of the next steps is to create SiO_2 isolations between islands with active devices. For this purpose, the surface of the wafer is oxidized with a thin layer of SiO_2. Then the entire wafer is covered with silicon nitride (Si_3N_4), which is also oxidized on its surface (Fig. 6-3 (a)). In the subsequent steps, an isolation mask (Fig. 6-3 (b)) is used to remove Si_3N_4 from the regions where SiO_2 insulation will be created (Fig. 6-3 (c)). Next (Fig. 6-3 (d)) the surface of the wafer is etched. Exposed silicon is dissolved while silicon covered with nitride remains unaffected. The etching is continued until the etched grooves are half the depth of the epitaxial layer.

After etching a boron implant is performed (Fig. 6-3 (e)). Silicon nitride stops dopant ions so that only silicon in the etched regions is affected. The goal of this operation is to increase the concentration of p-type impurities in the regions that will be covered with SiO_2. Such an increase is needed to prevent creation of a conducting p-channel in lightly doped n-type epitaxial layers.

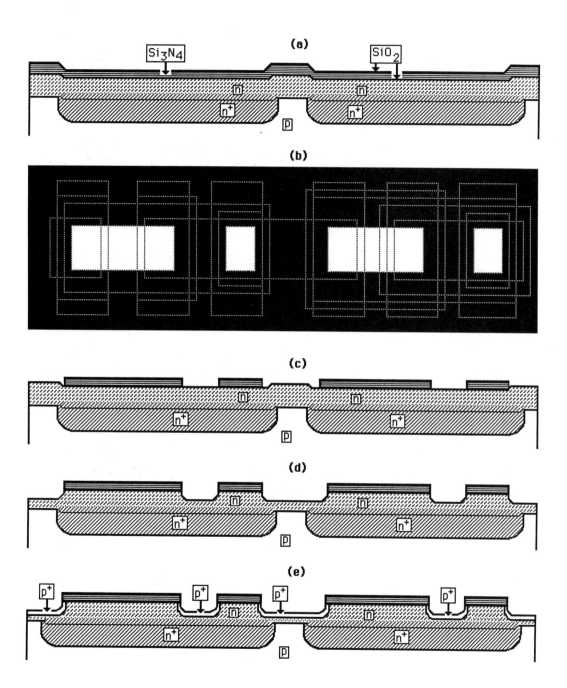

Figure 6-3: Advanced bipolar process. Part II.

The subsequent step, illustrated in Fig. 6-4, is oxidation. In this step a long, high-temperature cycle is used to grow a thick SiO_2 layer in the grooves in the silicon.

Note that the growing oxide consumes silicon and the SiO_2-Si interface thus penetrates the epitaxial layer. Eventually, SiO_2 is slightly thicker than the epitaxial layer and the SiO_2-Si interface is located in the substrate (see Fig. 6-4 (b)). In this way, islands of n-type regions are created. They are isolated from one another by SiO_2 walls and from the substrate by the p-n$^+$ junction.

The surface of the isolating field oxide is on the same level with the surface of the epitaxial layer (Fig. 6-4 (c)). This was achieved by using the previously described etching of the silicon. The only exceptions are the areas close to the edges of the isolation grooves where characteristic bird's beaks are created. The bird's beak effect is an inherent consequence of the selective oxidation applied in this process.

The subsequent processing step is shown in Fig. 6-4 (d) and (e). In this step phosphorus implantation is used to create n$^+$ regions connecting the surface of the wafer with the buried layer. Such connections are needed and will be used as contacts to the collectors of npn transistors and bases of pnp transistors. They are shown in Fig. 6-4 (d).

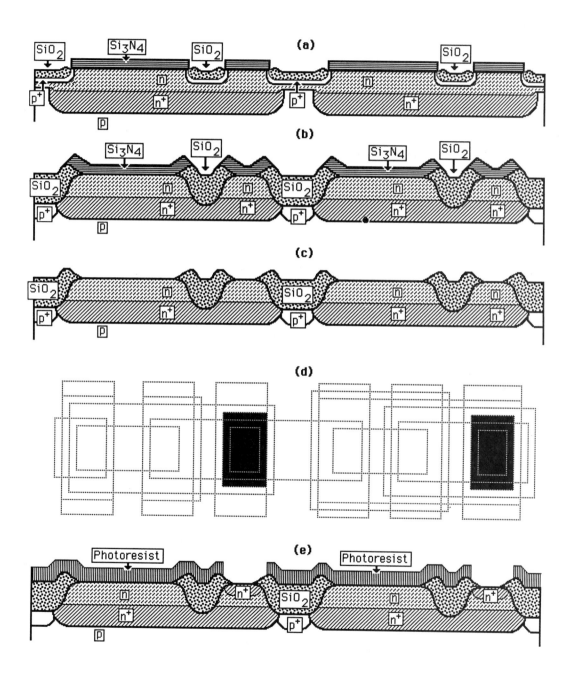

Figure 6-4: Advanced bipolar process. Part III.

After the n^+ contact implantation the entire surface of the wafer is again oxidized (Fig. 6-5 (a)). During this step phosphorus in the collector contact regions is rediffused so that the front of the diffusion reaches the edge of the buried layer.

The subsequent operation is the p-type dopant implant (Fig. 6-5 (c)). In this step boron is used to create bases of npn transistors and emitters and collectors of pnp transistors. The implantations are performed through the oxide using a photoresist layer patterned with the mask shown in Fig. 6-5 (b).

In the following step the contact mask shown in Fig. 6-5 (d) is used to remove SiO_2 from the regions in which contacts will be created.

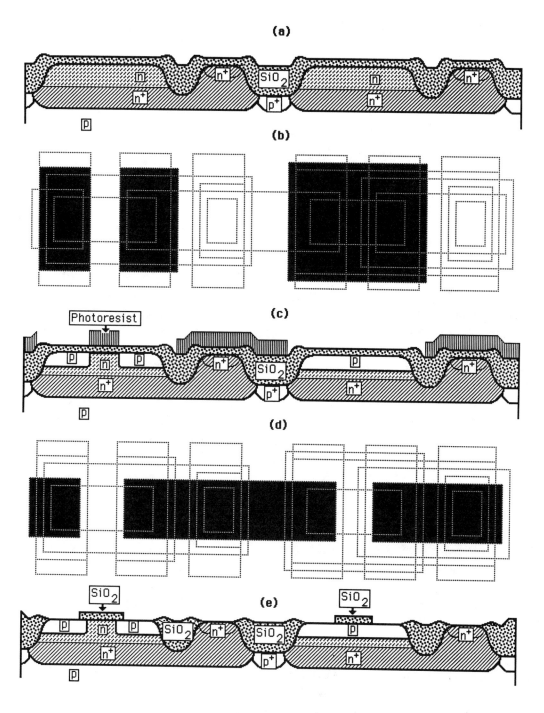

Figure 6-5: Advanced bipolar process. Part IV.

After contact lithography, the mask shown in Fig. 6-6 (a) and a layer of photoresist are used to form npn transistor emitters. A shallow n^+ phosphorus implant is used for this purpose. (The same mask and implant are used to dope collector contact regions.) Note that the photoresist protects previously open contact windows to the p-type regions.

In Fig. 6-6 (c) and (d) the metallization step is depicted. The mask used in this step is shown in Fig. 6-6 (c) and the cross-sectional view of the resulting structure is shown in Fig. 6-6 (d).

The final manufacturing steps in the process described above are the deposition of protecting overglass and lithography that opens windows to the bonding pads.

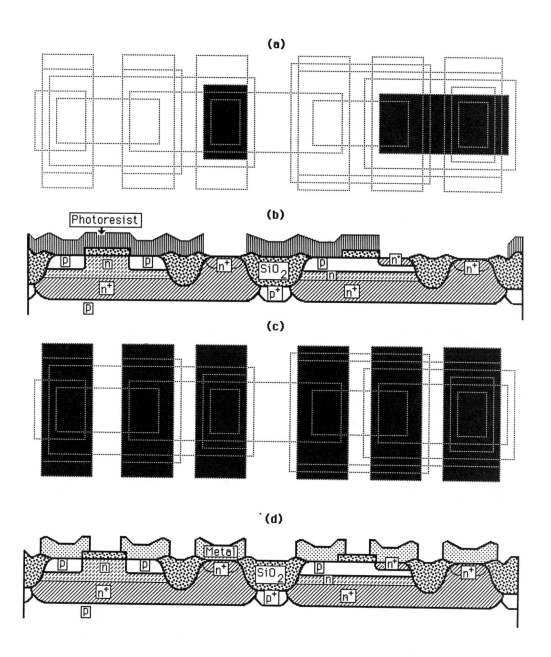

Figure 6-6: Advanced bipolar process. Part V.

6.2.2. Basic features of oxide-isolated bipolar devices

Fig. 6-7 summarizes the basic features of the IC devices fabricated with the bipolar process described in this chapter. Details of the layouts and the cross-sectional views of the npn and lateral pnp transistors are shown in Fig. 6-7 (a) and (c) and Fig. 6-7 (b), respectively.

Important features of these devices are:

- The side walls of the bases (and emitters and collectors of the pnp transistors) are formed by the dielectric.

- The emitter, base, and contact regions are self-aligned with respect to the oxide regions, which means that the locations of the boundaries of these regions are defined by the edges of the oxide regions rather than by the locations of the edges in the mask.

- The area of n^+-p^+ junction is greatly reduced compared to the area utilized in the standard bipolar process.

Note that the above features allow for a large increase in the scale of integration of bipolar circuits. Such an increase is possible because p regions (base) no longer have to be surrounded by the n (collector) region. In addition, selfalignment of the base and emitter regions allows for much tighter design rules.

The other advantage of the technology presented in this chapter is a significant decrease of the collector parasitic capacitance. This decrease contributes to the significant increase in speed of the bipolar technology that uses SiO_2 isolation.

Finally, it should be mentioned that the technology presented in this chapter is perhaps the simplest among the advanced bipolar technologies. The more complex bipolar processes, for example, apply doped polysilicon to form emitter regions. Two layers of metal are also possible enhancements of the process described in this chapter.

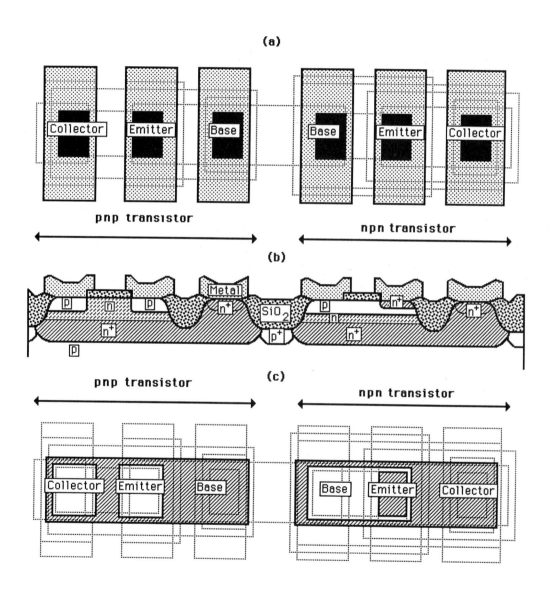

Figure 6-7: Advanced bipolar process.
Layout of the cell and cross-section
at the end of the process.

Chapter 7
Advanced NMOS Technology

The n-channel MOS processes such as the process described in Chapter 4 were very popular in the mid- and late-1970s. At the end of this period they were used to fabricate IC's with a transistor count approaching several tens of thousands.

In the early 1980s, progress in the optical and e-beam lithographies created an opportunity for a further increase in the scale of integration of the NMOS circuits. The new lithography and emerging etching techniques theoretically allowed fabrication of IC's containing a couple of hundreds of thousands of transistors.

It was found at the same time, however, that scaling the transistors' geometry up to the limits provided by new lithography techniques degraded important characteristics of fabricated devices, such as resistivity per square of conducting paths or the transistors' I-V characteristic.

This chapter presents improvements introduced to the traditional NMOS process that transform the older NMOS technology into an advanced process. These improvements allow for the effective scaling of the n-channel transistors. They have been found so effective that they are commonly applied not only in NMOS processes but also in many advanced CMOS processes.

7.1. The transistor scaling problem

A larger density, i.e. larger scale of integration, of an IC is achievable through a decrease of the horizontal dimensions of the IC components. A very basic problem with the decrease of horizontal dimensions of IC devices is that they cannot be scaled independently of their vertical dimensions. As is shown in the further part of this section, the scaling of both vertical and horizontal dimensions of MOS transistors is not a trivial task and involves careful consideration of the process and device physics.

Fig. 7-1 illustrates a couple of approaches that can be used to scale an NMOS transistor such as the one in Fig. 7-1 (a). Fig. 7-1 (b) shows the situation in which all dimensions are scaled down by the same factor (in this case 2). It is assumed that the scaling of the drain and source junction depth X_j requires a decrease of the surface concentration of the dopant. It is obvious that this kind of scaling results in a drastic increase in the resistivity of the source and drain regions and that this increase is due to both the shallower junction and the decrease of the surface concentration C_s.

Fig. 7-1 (c) illustrates a scaling that is supposed to preserve the value of the sheet resistance of the drain and source regions. In such a scaling the horizontal dimension and oxide thickness t_{ox} are scaled down by the same factor while the junction depth and dopant profile remain unchanged. Of course, such a procedure leads to unacceptable short channels.

The third possibility is illustrated in Fig. 7-1 (d), where a scaled-down transistor with acceptable sheet resistivity of the drain and source regions is depicted. Such scaling is achieved by shrinking all dimensions of the transistor. The decrease of X_j, however, is compensated by the increased surface concentration of the dopant. Unfortunately this structure also has a problem, caused by the high gradient of the dopant in the junction region. The dopant gradient is much higher than in the original device due to the shallower junction and higher C_s. It generates a large electrical field that is responsible for a "hot electron" effect. Such an effect degrades the transistors' I-V characteristic and also leads to reliability problems.

Thus, scaling of the transistor dimensions cannot be achieved by simply shrinking the IC layout. It has to involve process changes that allow preservation of acceptable values of sheet resistances of conducting layers without an increase in the electrical field in the drain regions. The next section discusses an NMOS process that includes such changes and therefore allows for the effective scaling of IC devices.

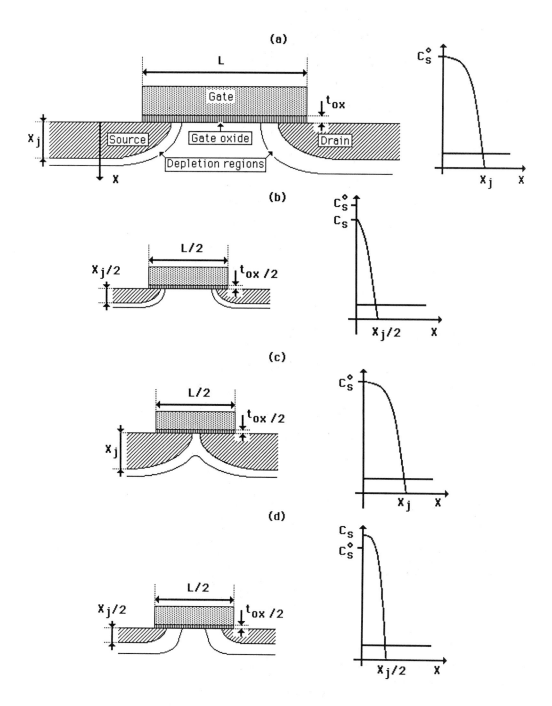

Figure 7-1: Various transistor scaling schemas.

7.2. The silicon gate n-channel technology

7.2.1. Process

The advanced NMOS process usually starts with a lightly doped, p-type, $<100>$ oriented substrate. The surface of such a substrate is covered with a layer of silicon nitride (Si_3N_4) that is patterned with an active region mask (Fig. 7-2 (a)).

After active region lithography, p^+ dopant is used and channel-stop regions are implanted (Fig. 7-2 (b)). Next, the silicon nitride is used to selectively grow a thick layer of field oxide Fig. 7-2 (c)). After the field oxidation silicon nitride is removed and active regions (black regions in the mask in Fig. 7-2 (a)) are open for further processing.

In the subsequent steps the transistors' channels are formed. First, a thin layer of thermal protective oxide is grown in the active regions (Fig. 7-2 (d)). Then the wafer is covered with a thick layer of photoresist and a lithography step using the mask shown in Fig. 7-2 (e) is performed. This lithography is supposed to protect some active region areas during subsequent implantation steps.

In the next step, illustrated in Fig. 7-2 (e) and referred to as the **threshold adjustment implant,** a boron dopant is used to increase the concentration of p-type impurities in the active regions unprotected by the photoresist. The goal of this step is to determine the threshold voltage of the enhancement mode transistors.

The transistors that will be created in the active regions covered with photoresist will have a threshold voltage lower than that of the enhancement mode transistors. The threshold voltage of the transistors in the active regions covered with photoresist is determined by the concentration of the p-type dopant in the substrate and usually is around zero volts.

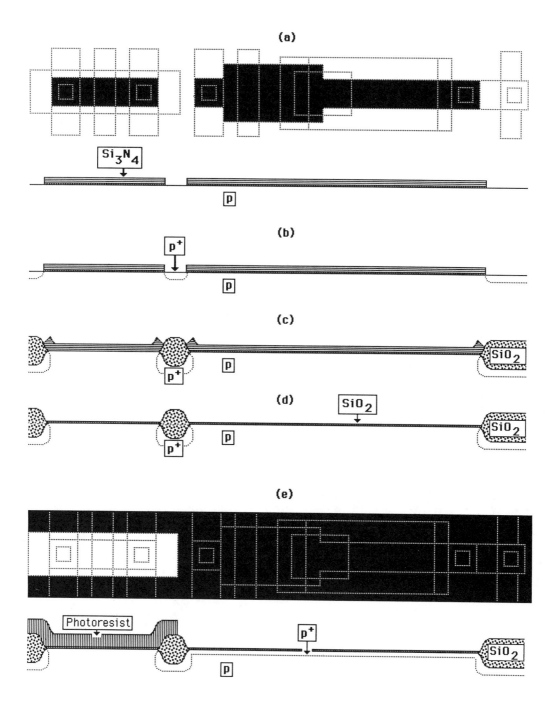

Figure 7-2: Advanced NMOS process. Part I.

In the next step, illustrated in Fig. 7-3 (a), implantation of phosphorus or arsenic is used to set the threshold voltage of the depletion mode transistors. The windows in the photoresist are patterned in such a way that the n-type dopant ions are introduced into the channels of the depletion devices.

Then the thin layer of protective oxide is removed and another layer of oxide is thermally grown (Fig. 7-3 (b)). This layer is used as a gate insulator. It is patterned with the buried contact mask shown in Fig. 7-3 (c). As in the traditional NMOS process, buried contacts are used to form connections between the polysilicon layer and the n^+ regions in the substrate.

After the buried contact lithography the entire wafer is covered with polysilicon. The **low pressure chemical vapor deposition (LPCVD)** technique is usually used for this purpose (Fig. 7-3 (d)). The polysilicon deposition is followed by a step in which the layer of polysilicon is heavily doped with phosphorus. Such doping is needed to decrease the sheet resistance of the polysilicon. These steps are usually performed at high temperatures as a predeposition step, so phosphorus diffuses through the polysilicon and dopes the substrate in the buried contact windows (see Fig. 7-3 (d)).

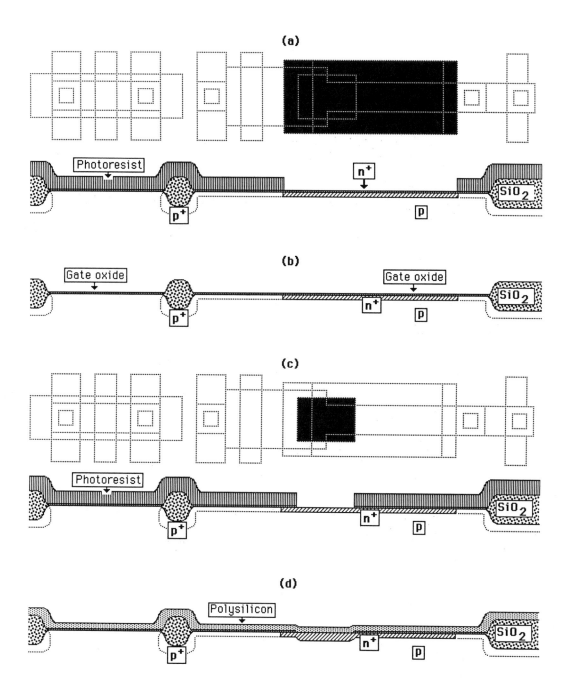

Figure 7-3: Advanced NMOS process. Part II.

In the subsequent step the mask shown in Fig. 7-4 (a) and photoresist are used to form transistor gates and polysilicon connections. After this step transistor channels with three different doping levels are completely formed (see Fig. 7-4 (b)).

The next steps are different from the processing operation explained in Chapter 4. They are applied to build so-called **lightly doped drain (LDD)** structures, which are supposed to solve the transistor scaling problem mentioned in the previous section.

The LDD structures are formed such that source and drain regions are created using two different implantation steps. First, phosphorus is implanted (Fig. 7-4 (c)) so that lightly doped, very shallow drain and source n-type regions are formed. Then, the entire wafer is covered with a low-temperature oxide (LTO) (Fig. 7-4 (d)). The LTO is removed using anisotropic plasma (dry) etching. Such etching does not remove SiO_2 from the side walls of the polysilicon paths. (Details are discussed in Section 7.2.2.) In this way, **side wall spacers** are created (Fig. 7-4 (e)).

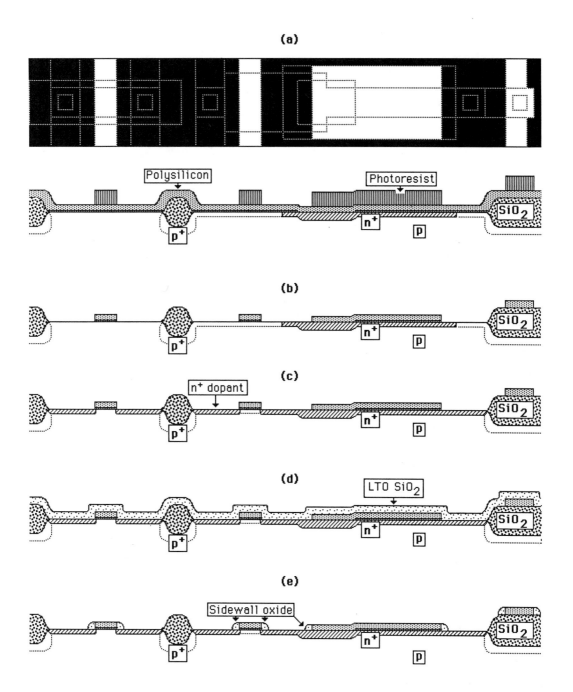

Figure 7-4: Advanced NMOS process. Part III

In the last step of the source-drain formation process an arsenic or antimony implant is used to dope source and drain regions again (Fig. 7-5 (a)). A large dose of dopant is used to minimize the sheet resistance of these regions. Note that at this step the regions that are masked by the polysilicon gates are extended by the sidewall spacers, so that the fronts of the lateral edges of the implanted regions do not reach the edges of the transistor channels. Thus, the edges of the drain and source regions adjacent to the channels are lightly doped while at the same time large portions of source and drain regions have low resistivity.

The remaining part of the process discussed in this chapter is identical to the process described in Chapter 4. Thus, after the drain-source implant the wafer is covered with CVD LTO and then contact holes are formed (Fig. 7-5 (b) and (c)). Finally, metal connections are created (Fig. 7-5 (d)) and the wafer is covered with an overglass layer which is patterned to open windows to the bounding pads.

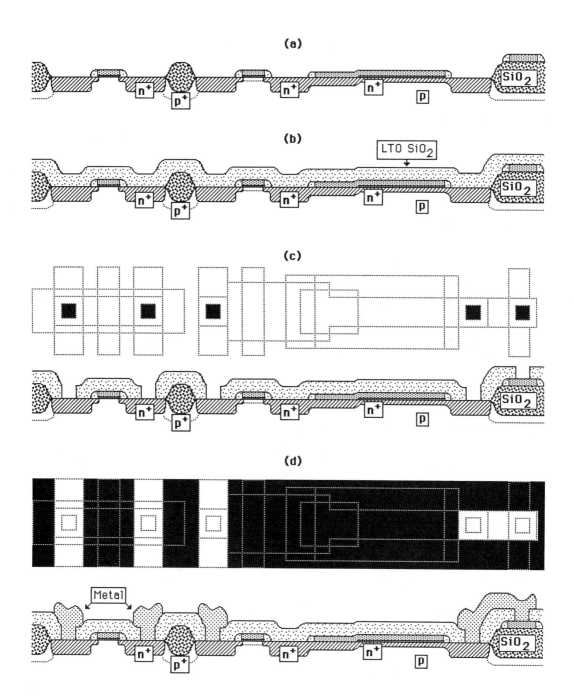

Figure 7-5:   Advanced NMOS process. Part IV.

7.2.2. Basic features of the advanced NMOS technology

Fig. 7-6 summarizes the basic features of the NMOS technology discussed in this chapter. Important enhancements of this process are:

- Zero threshold voltage transistors;

- Lightly doped drain extensions; and

- Implanted drains and sources.

The last two features allow for effective scaling of the transistor channels and thus for a significant increase in the scale of integration of the traditional NMOS process.

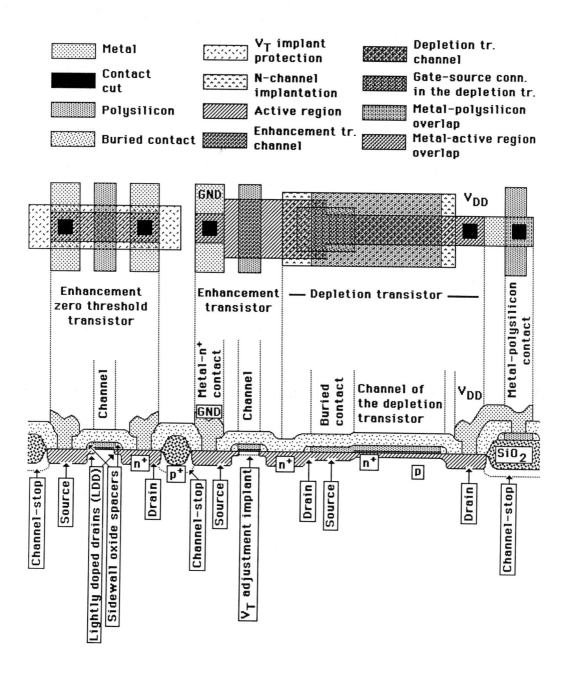

Figure 7-6: Summary of the basic features of the
advanced n-channel MOS process.

Especially important improvements in the advanced NMOS process are due to the introduction of the LDD structures. They are important because they allow fabrication of very small transistors that do not suffer from "hot electron" phenomena.

Fig. 7-7 summarizes the process features that lead to the formation of the LDD transistor structures. Fig. 7-7 (a) and (b) show the transistor cross-section before and after the first drain-source implant. Fig. 7-7 (c) and (d) illustrate the formation of the LTO layer. Note that oxide is deposited uniformly on the entire surface including the side walls of the polysilicon path. The most important step of the LDD formation is the etching shown in Fig. 7-7 (e). At this step SiO_2 is anisotropically etched so that the oxide deposited on the side walls of the polysilicon is unaffected (Fig. 7-7 (f)). This way the location of the lateral edges of the regions implanted in the subsequent step is determined by the location of the polysilicon and the width of the side wall oxide (Fig. 7-7 (g)). Thus the gate does not overlap with heavily doped source-drain regions (Fig. 7-7 (h)) and LDD structures ensure a low dopant gradient in the drain-channel interface (Fig. 7-7 (i)).

The LDD devices thus minimize high electrical fields at the drain-channel and source-channel interfaces. (In addition they assure a minimal value of the gate-source capacitances.) These features combined with the simplicity of the NMOS process and the advantages of zero threshold voltage transistors maintain the advanced NMOS process described in this chapter as a very attractive alternative for a lot of VLSI applications.

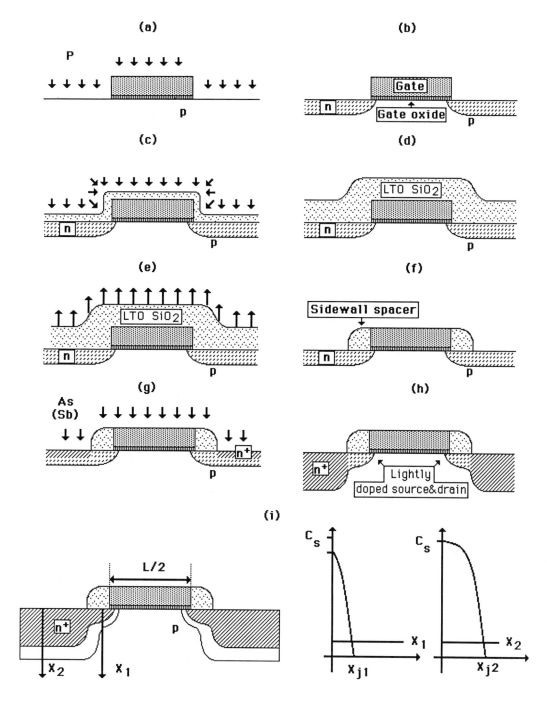

Figure 7-7: Formation of the LDD transistor structure.

Chapter 8
Advanced CMOS Technologies

The description in Chapter 5 illustrates basic fabrication steps in the standard simple n-well CMOS process. It was presented in this book in order to introduce the basic concept of the CMOS process.

The actual CMOS processes, however, may be quite different from the process presented in Chapter 5. A p-well process or any advanced CMOS process is organized differently from the n-well process discussed there. Thus, further studies of various versions of the CMOS process as well as discussion of some processing sequences and technological details seem necessary for a better understanding of the complexity and the advantages of modern CMOS technology.

The goal of this chapter is to present two more CMOS processes: the standard simple p-well process and the advanced twin-tub process. They are used to explain trends in CMOS process evolution as a consequence of the need for larger-scale integration of CMOS circuits.

8.1. The MOSIS process

8.1.1. Semiconductor brokerage operation

MOSIS is an acronym for **MOS** **I**mplementation **S**ervice which is an organization that provides university communities with IC fabrication services. It was set up by DARPA in 1981 in order to promote VLSI design activities in universities.

MOSIS acts as an interface between university designers and semiconductor houses. It collects designs from various design groups, transforms them into the needed form and sends them to the semiconductor vendors. MOSIS cooperates with various vendors that fabricate designs submitted to MOSIS. All the designs, regardless of the fabricator, are designed using the same set of design rules and the same "notion of the fabrication process." Three processes are available to the MOSIS communities: standard NMOS[*], standard CMOS, and advanced CMOS.

In this section the concept of a standard MOSIS p-well CMOS process is presented. It was recreated from information provided by MOSIS and can be executed by different vendors. Thus, the MOSIS process presented in the next section can be seen by a designer as an actual technology even if it is executed in a slightly different manner by the different vendors.

8.1.2. The MOSIS p-well technology

The MOSIS standard p-well process starts with the oxidation of an n-type substrate (Fig. 8-1 (a)). Then, the p-well mask is used to open windows in the SiO_2 (Fig. 8-1 (b)). A high-energy, large-dose implant of boron is used to introduce a p^+ dopant through these windows (Fig. 8-1 (c)). The dopant is subsequently rediffused in a high-temperature step (Fig. 8-1 (d)) to form the p-wells (Fig. 8-1 (e)).

---

[*]Described in Chapter 4

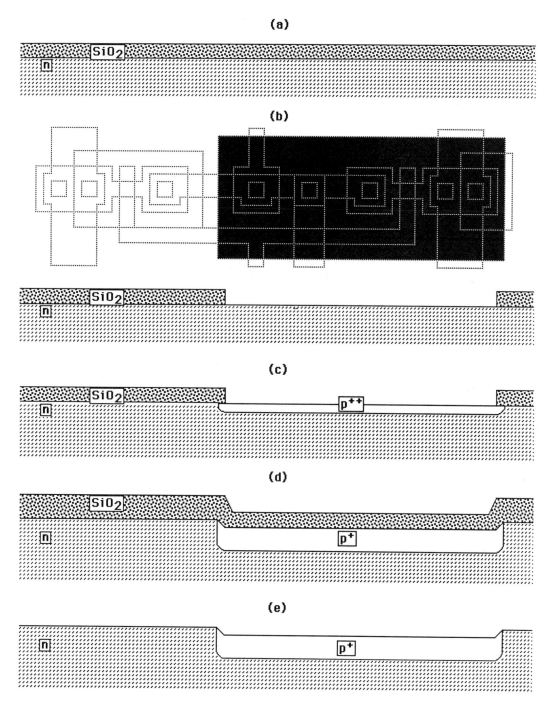

Figure 8-1: MOSIS CMOS process. Part I.

In the subsequent steps a standard sequence of operations is used to create active regions. The active region mask shown in Fig. 8-2 (a) is used to pattern a layer of silicon nitride. (Then a field arsenic implant may be applied to form channel-stop n^+ regions in the lightly doped n-type substrate. See Fig. 8-2 (b). In the simplest version of this process the channel-stop implant may be skipped, however.) Afterwards, a thick layer of field oxide is grown and $Si_3 N_4$ is stripped off.

At that moment (Fig. 8-2 (c)) a threshold adjustment implant may be used to control the dopant concentration of both n-channel and p-channel devices. If boron is used then the threshold voltage of the n-channel device (to be created in the p-well) can be increased and the threshold voltage of the p-channel device can be shifted towards less negative values. A phosphorus implant causes opposite changes. A thin layer of thermally grown SiO_2, not shown in Fig. 8-2 (c), may be used during the implantation to reduce surface damage. Finally, a thin layer of gate oxide is thermally grown (Fig. 8-2 (d)).

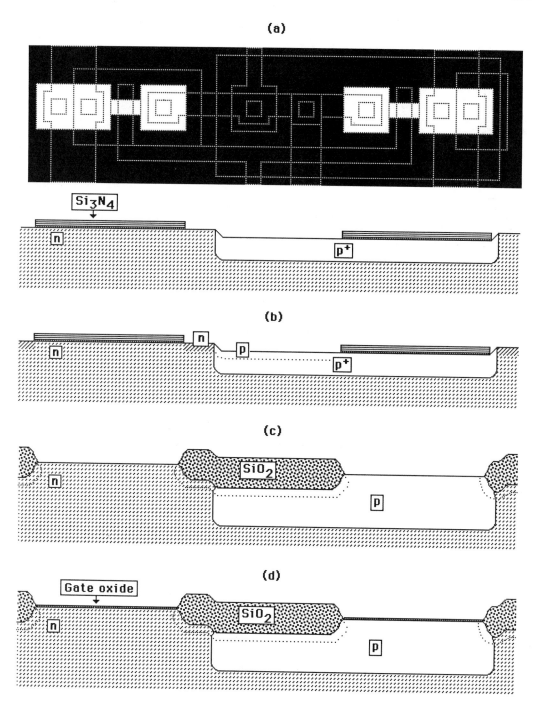

Figure 8-2: MOSIS CMOS process. Part II.

In the next step the wafer is covered with a highly doped n^+ polysilicon layer that is patterned with the mask shown in Fig. 8-3 (a). Then the n-select mask is used to open windows in the thick layer of photoresist in the drain and source regions of p-channel transistors and to form contacts to the p-well (Fig. 8-3 (b)). Next a boron implantation is performed and the photoresist is stripped off.

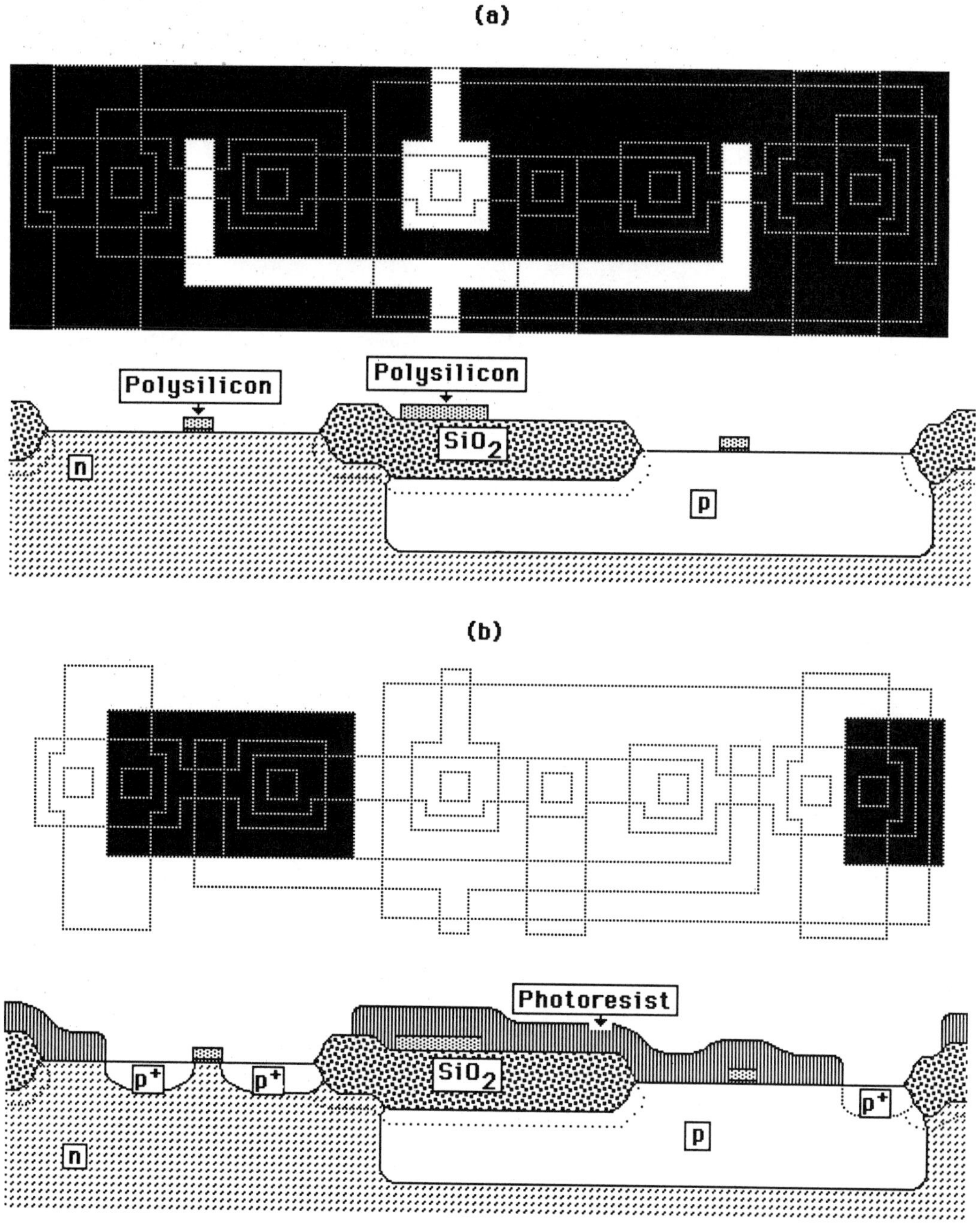

(a)

(b)

Figure 8-3: MOSIS CMOS process. Part III.

The negative of the n-select mask that was used in the previous step is employed to form sources and drains of n-channel transistors and contacts to the substrate (see Fig. 8-4 (a)).

After formation of the basic transistor structures the entire wafer is covered with CVD low temperature oxide (LTO) (Fig. 8-4(b)) in which contact cuts are etched. Fig. 8-4 (c) shows the mask used for this purpose and the cross-section of the inverter after contact etching. Note that the oxide is opened to n^+, p^+, and polysilicon regions.

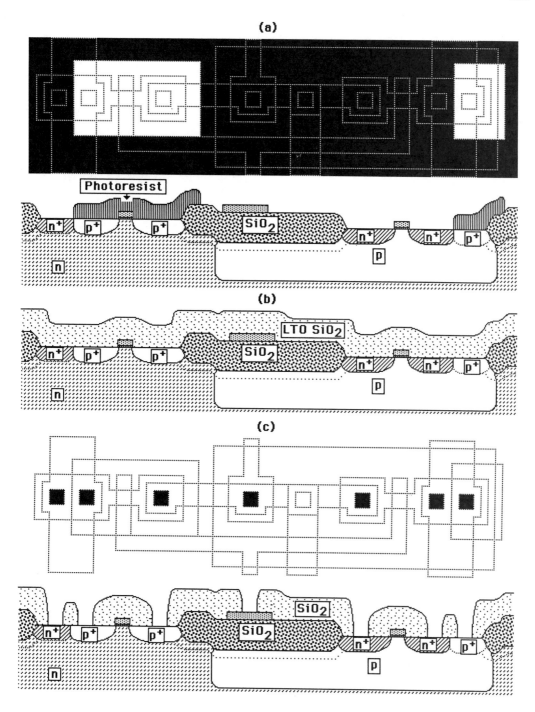

Figure 8-4: MOSIS CMOS process. Part IV.

In the subsequent steps metal connections are defined. First the wafer is covered with a layer of aluminum (Fig. 8-5 (a)) and then a metallization mask shown in Fig. 8-5 (b) is used to form connections.

After the metallization steps the wafer is covered with another layer of LTO SiO_2 (Fig. 8-5 (c)).

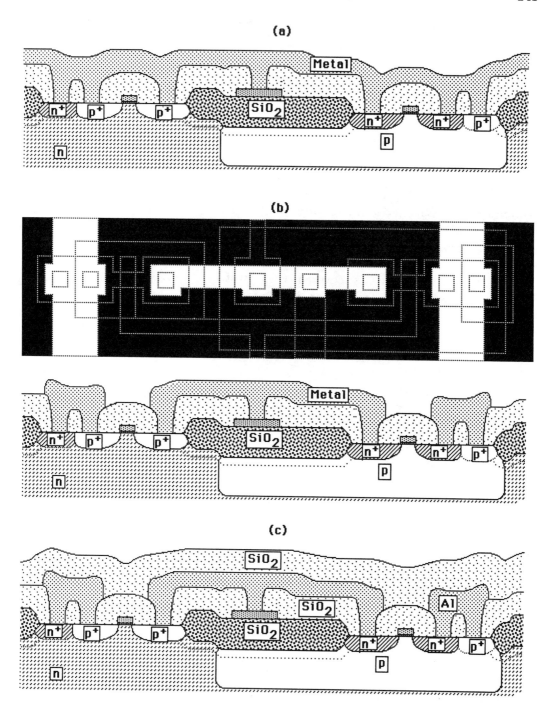

Figure 8-5: MOSIS CMOS process. Part V.

To form connections between the two layers of metal another contact mask (shown in Fig. 8-6 (a)) is used. Then the wafer is covered with another layer of aluminum that is patterned with the mask shown in Fig. 8-6(b).

Finally, the entire wafer is covered with protective overglass (not shown in Fig. 8-6) and windows to the bounding pads are etched.

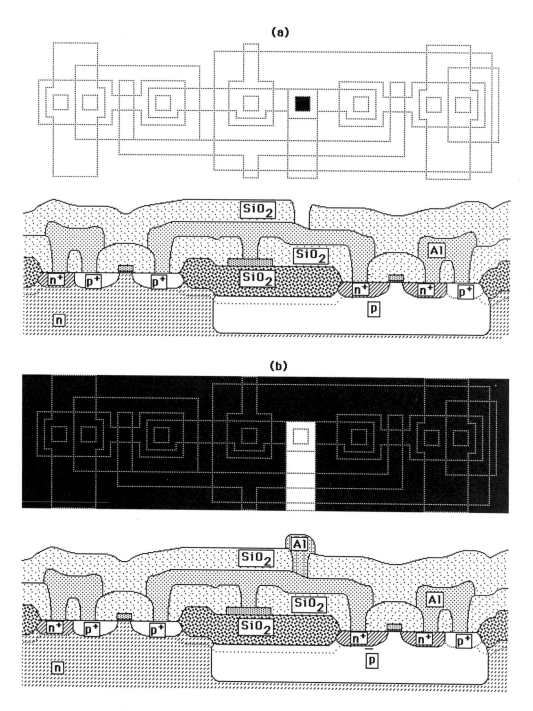

Figure 8-6: MOSIS CMOS process. Part VI.

8.1.3. Summary of the basic characteristics of the MOSIS CMOS process

Fig. 8-7 summarizes the basic features of the standard MOSIS CMOS process showing the layout and cross-section of an inverter. The basic characteristics of this process are as follows:

- It is a p-well process;

- It provides three layers of connections: one poly and two metals;

- It offers medium-scale integration because it uses very simple transistor structures; and

- It requires that the p-wells and the substrate are connected to V_{SS} and V_{DD}, respectively. Such connections are needed to prevent latchup, as is discussed in more detail in Section 8.2.1.

The standard MOSIS CMOS process can be an excellent vehicle for the implementation of large circuits, but its capabilities are limited because of its simplicity.

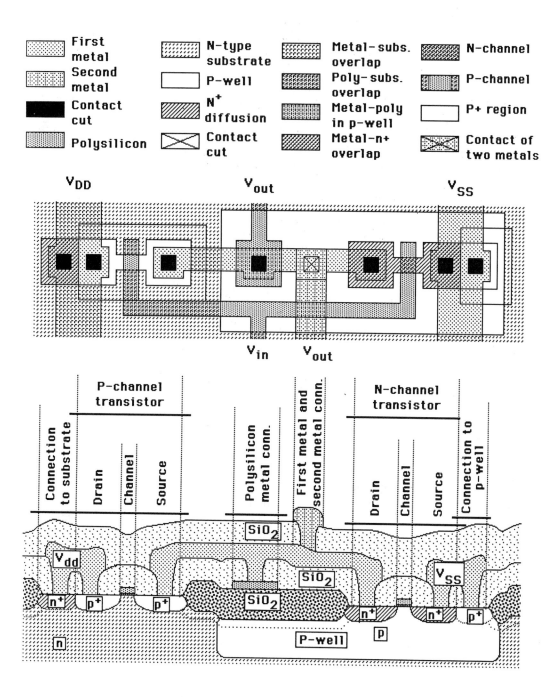

Figure 8-7: Basic features of the standard p-well MOSIS process.

8.2. The advanced twin-tub CMOS process

The CMOS technology described in the previous section is very attractive mainly because of the low power consumption. The disadvantage of this technology is that many components are needed to implement basic logic functions. As is shown in the next subsection, a CMOS circuit fabricated in this technology requires a special well and substrate grounding schema that also occupies a lot of silicon area. The main effort in the development of new CMOS processes is therefore devoted to process enhancements that allow better area utilization.

This section describes an advanced CMOS process in which a high circuit density is achieved through a scaling of the transistors and through a process optimization that prevents the so-called "latchup" effect.

8.2.1. Latchup

A **latchup** is a condition of the IC that causes a short circuit between the V_{DD} and V_{SS} lines. Such a short is caused by parasitic devices that are inherent components of any CMOS circuit. The mechanism of latchup is explained in Fig. 8-8 and Fig. 8-9.

The latchup is caused by the **parasitic thyristor** which is composed of the npn and pnp transistors. Fig. 8-8 shows such a structure in the standard p-well CMOS inverter depicted in Fig. 8-8 (a). The npn parasitic transistor (see Fig. 8-8 (b)) is formed by the drain of the n-channel transistor (emitter), p-well (base), and substrate (collector). The pnp transistor is formed by the drain of the p-channel transistor (emitter), substrate (base), and p-well (collector) (see Fig. 8-8 (c)). The resulting structure forms the thyristor structure shown in Fig. 8-8 (d).

Note also that assuming that the inverter's output is low (V_{SS}), the inverter structure can be seen as the pnpn structure shown in Fig. 8-8 (d). Such a structure is used to explain conditions that lead to the large current between V_{DD} and V_{SS} nodes, i.e. to the latchup effect.

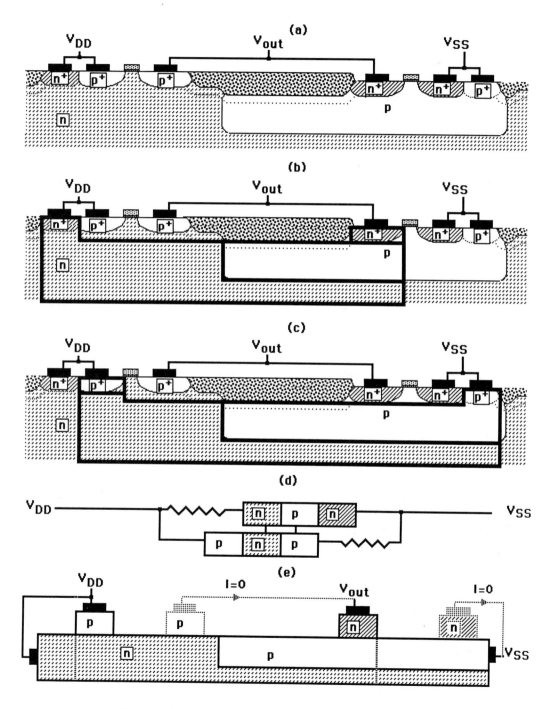

Figure 8-8: Parasitic npn and pnp transistors in
the p-well CMOS inverter.

Note that the p-well CMOS inverter with $V_{out} = V_{SS}$ can be seen as the structure shown in Fig. 8-9. Assume also that the voltage drop U_1 is larger than U_2 (Fig. 8-9 (b)) and that $U_1 - U_2 > 0.6$ V. Under these conditions, which are quite realistic, the emitter junction of the npn transistor (highlighted with the thicker line) is forward biased. Thus it injects a large amount of electrons into the base (p-well). These electrons recombine in the p-well and in the substrate, and some of them reach the V_{DD}-substrate contact. The electron current in the substrate causes voltage drop U_3, which may cause a forward bias of the p-n junction of the emitter of the pnp parasitic transistor. This junction injects holes into the substrate (see Fig. 8-9 (c)) that form a hole component of the current in the p-well that recombines on the V_{SS} contact. Such a current causes an increase of U_1 and a further increase of the electron current in the substrate. Hence, the positive feedback occurs between U_1 and U_3, and consequently current between V_{DD} and V_{SS} may reach a level causing destruction of the inverter.

Thus any situation that causes the drain of the n-channel transistor to be forward biased with respect to the p-well launches the positive feedback that results in the latchup effect.

A similar effect can occur when $V_{out} = V_{DD}$. In this case also, forward bias of the source-substrate junction of the p-channel transistor may trigger positive feedback, thus resulting in the latchup.

These considerations directly indicate that in order to prevent latchup it is necessary to create conditions that minimize the chances of positive feedback causing lateral voltage drops between the contact to the p-well and drain of the n-channel transistor and the contact to the substrate and source of the p-channel transistor. This can be achieved by increasing the distance L (Fig. 8-9 (a)), using additional contacts called **guard rings** (shown in Fig. 8-9 (e)), or by changing the technology in such a way that lateral voltage drops are minimal.

Note that the means of latchup prevention available with the standard p-well processes lead to a decrease of the layout density. This indicates that larger-scale integration of CMOS circuits must be achieved by process improvements rather than through layout modifications.

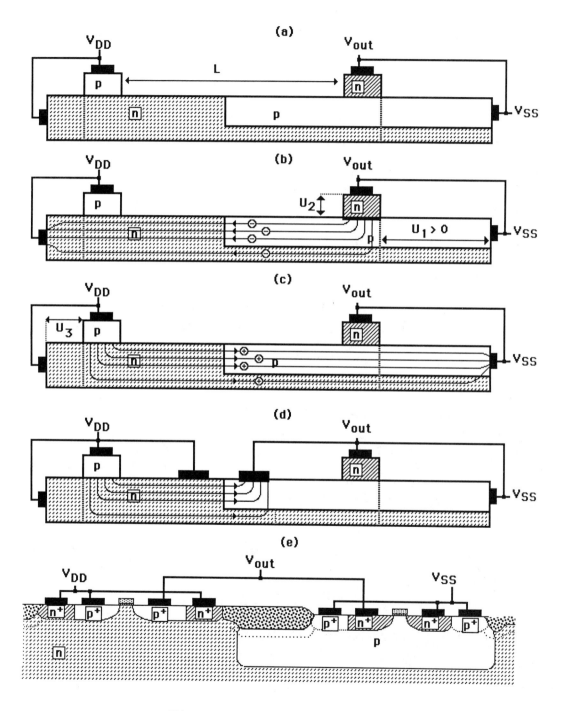

Figure 8-9: Latchup mechanism.

8.2.2. The advanced twin-tub CMOS process

A main concept behind the advanced CMOS processes is the application of n-channel and p-channel transistors created in two separate **tubs** (tanks or wells) that are formed in separate processing steps. This simple modification of the standard process allows independent control of the threshold voltages of both transistors and keeps resistivity of the wells on such a level that lateral voltage drops within the wells are small.

The advanced CMOS process described in this section uses lightly doped n-type substrate. (An n-type substrate with a lightly doped epitaxial layer can also be used for this purpose.) At the beginning of the process such a substrate is oxidized and then etched with a p-well mask. After etching (Fig. 8-10 (a)) a high-energy, large-dose boron implant is used to form a source for the p-well diffusion step shown in Fig. 8-10 (b). After p-well diffusion SiO_2 is stripped off (Fig. 8-10 (c)) and the n-well mask is used to open windows in the thick photoresist for the n-well implantation step. (Fig. 8-10 (d)).

After implantation of the n-well the active regions are formed using a layer of silicon nitride. After patterning of the silicon nitride (Fig. 8-10 (e)) a boron implant is used to form channel-stop regions (Fig. 8-10 (f)). Finally, a layer of thick field oxide is thermally grown (Fig. 8-10 (g)). Note that during this step both the p-well and the n-well are rediffused deeper into the substrate.

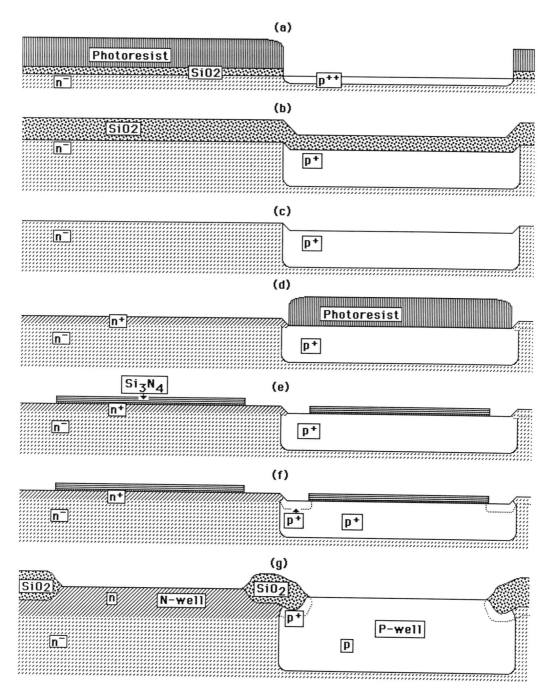

Figure 8-10: Advanced CMOS process. Part I.

In the subsequent step a gate oxide is grown inside the active regions (Fig. 8-11 (a)) and then polysilicon is deposited and patterned using the polysilicon mask (Fig. 8-11 (b)).

The next sequence of steps is used to form LDD structures. First a phosphorus implant is used to define shallow n^+ regions (Fig. 8-11 (c)). Then the wafer is covered with LPCVD oxide (Fig. 8-11 (d)) that is etched such that SiO_2 sidewall spacers are formed (Fig. 8-11 (e)).

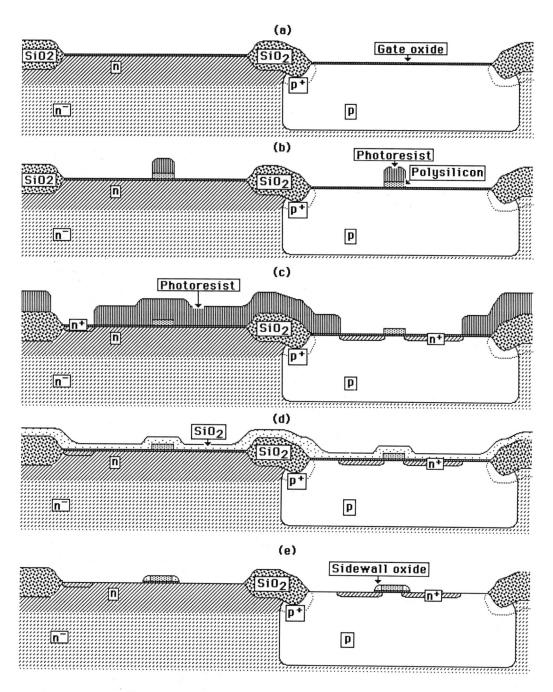

Figure 8-11: Advanced CMOS process. Part II.

Next a thin layer of SiO_2 is grown inside the active regions (Fig. 8-12 (a)). It is used to protect the surface of the substrate during the subsequent implantations.

The next operations are two implantation steps. In the first step the n-select mask and antimony or arsenic dopant are used to form the n^+ source, drain, and contact region (Fig. 8-12 (b)). (It is important to remember that Sb and As are dopants that diffuse one order of magnitude more slowly than phosphorus and boron.) Then the negative of the n-select mask and a boron dopant are used to create sources and drains of the p-channel transistors and a contact to the p-well (Fig. 8-12 (c)). Both implantation steps are followed by thermal annealing during which both phosphorus and boron diffuse, thus shifting the lateral edges of the drains and sources. Due to the larger diffusivity of boron, the edges of the p-channel are moving faster than the edges of the sources and drains of the n-channel transistors. Consequently, the overlap of the gate with heavily doped portions of sources and drains is much smaller in the n-channel transistors than in the p-channel transistors.

After the transistors are formed the entire wafer is covered with another layer of LTO SiO_2 (Fig. 8-12(d)).

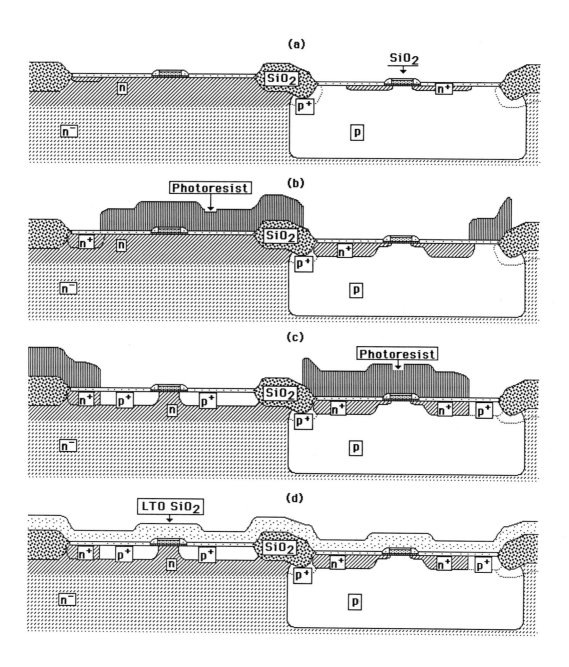

Figure 8-12: Advanced CMOS process. Part III.

This layer of LTO is then etched to open contacts (Fig. 8-13 (a)) and the wafer is covered with a layer of aluminum. (Alloys of Al, Mo, and W may also be used.) This layer is referred to as the **first metal** and is patterned to form basic connections in the circuit (Fig. 8-13 (b)). Since in the described technology large-scale integration is possible, the surface of the IC fabricated with this process may be very rough. Therefore, the surface of the IC has to be **planarized** before deposition of another layer of metal. Such a planarization is performed in the following way. First (see Fig. 8-13 (c)) the wafer is covered with a very thick layer of SiO_2. Then a thick layer of photoresist is spun on top of the SiO_2 layer. Since photoresist is deposited in liquid form its surface is flat.

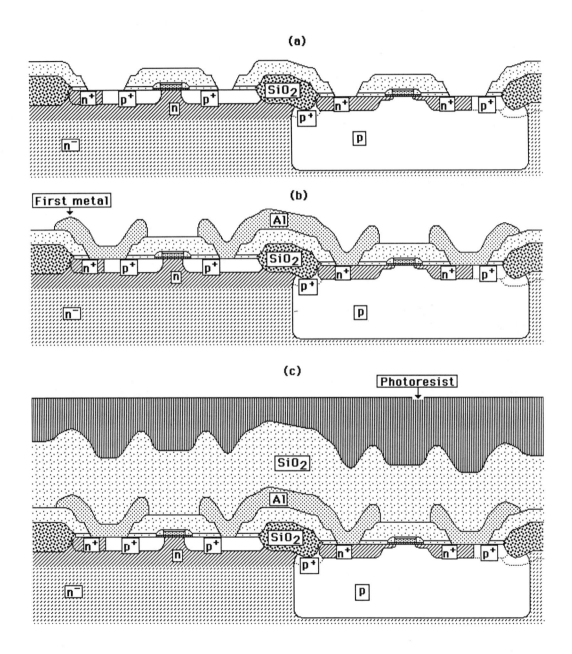

Figure 8-13: Advanced CMOS process. Part IV.

Subsequently the photoresist is etched with a solution that has the same etching rate for photoresist and SiO_2. If etching is performed long enough a flat surface of SiO_2 can thus be achieved (see Fig. 8-14(a)).

After etching, another protective layer of SiO_2 is deposited (Fig. 8-14 (b)) and the standard contact lithography, the second metal deposition, and lithography are carried out (see Fig. 8-14 (c)).

At the end of the process the wafer is covered with a protective layer of overglass and windows to the bounding pads are etched.

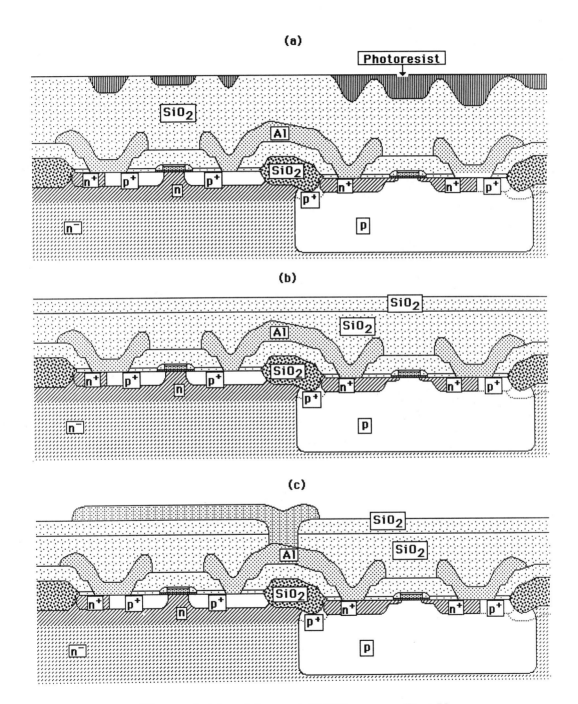

Figure 8-14: Advanced CMOS process. Part V.

8.2.3. Basic features of the advanced CMOS process

Fig. 8-15 summarizes the basic characteristics of the CMOS technology presented in this section. This technology provides:

- Two layers of metal connections, both of them of high quality due to the planarization step;

- Optimal threshold voltages of both p-channel and n-channel transistors, achieved through the double-well process;

- LDD n-channel transistors preventing hot-electron phenomena; and

- Good latchup protection achieved by minimization of the lateral voltage drops inside the wells.

So the process presented above offers significant improvements over the traditional CMOS process. It must be mentioned, however, that some additional improvements are possible. Some of them are discussed in Chapter 9.

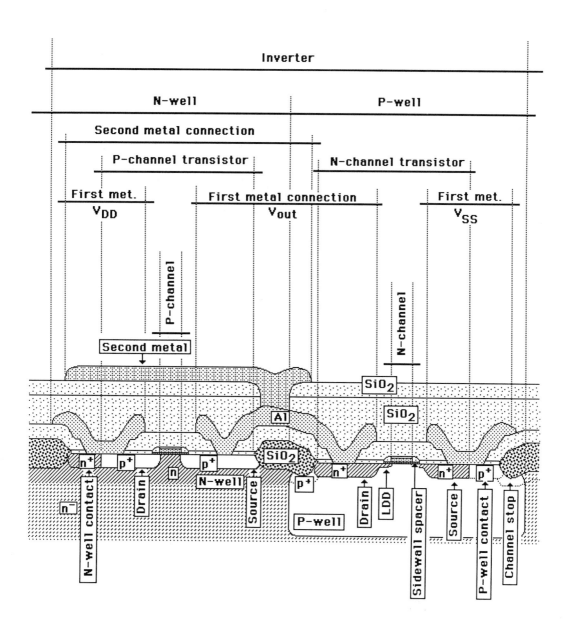

Figure 8-15: The Advanced CMOS process. Summary of basic features.

Chapter 9
Mixed Bipolar-MOS Technology

It seems evident that the advanced CMOS processes will be the most popular choices for the majority of VLSI applications. The CMOS technologies provide the lowest possible levels of power consumption, the speed of the CMOS logic approaches the speed of the bipolar circuit, and the technology-driven latchup prevention schemes allow achievement of very dense CMOS layouts.

It has also been demonstrated recently that by some modifications of the CMOS process it is possible to fabricate a CMOS circuit containing bipolar transistors. Thus the CMOS process will perhaps evolve into a **bipolar-CMOS (BiMOS)** process that will provide the best features of both the bipolar and the CMOS worlds. It is anticipated that with such a technology large analog-digital systems will be fabricated on a common substrate. (Some CMOS memories already use bipolar devices in sense amplifiers or drivers.)

The goal of this chapter is to introduce the basic concept of the BiMOS process. A simple version was chosen in order to illustrate the main idea of the bipolar-CMOS merger only. It must be stressed, however, that the majority of the BiMOS processes described in the literature are very complex. They usually use several additional masks. (For example, a process using 16 masks is not unusual, while a simple NMOS process can be performed with 5 masks.) They also apply a lot of advanced processing techniques.

9.1. Bipolar transistors in the CMOS circuit

As was indicated in the discussion of the latchup problem, CMOS circuits contain bipolar pnp and npn transistors. Their parameters and their structure, however, do not allow their use as components of IC functional blocks. The one exception is a lateral npn transistor that can be created by small changes in the layout of the n-channel transistor. Fig. 9-1 explains the main concept of such a modification. Fig. 9-1 (a) shows the cross-section of a p-well CMOS inverter. Fig. 9-1 (b) depicts a modification of the n-channel transistor which actually is a lateral npn transistor. In this alternative the p-well is used as an isolation island and the collector and emitter are created during the formation of the n-channel transistor drains and sources. Unfortunately a transistor of this kind can be used for a limited number of applications because it has a low current gain (β) and bad I-V characteristics.

Another version of a bipolar transistor that can be fabricated with the CMOS process is the vertical pnp transistor shown in Fig. 9-1 (c). The p-well is used as a collector in this transistor. The n^+ drain-source implant is used to form the base region and the p^+ drain-source implant is applied to create the emitter. Note that such a pnp transistor will have a reasonably stable β if, and only if, the junction depth of the n^+ region is significantly deeper than the junction depth of the p^+ region. But this means that the original CMOS process must be modified and n-channel transistors have to be enlarged. Of course, such an alteration is unacceptable.

Thus, a traditional CMOS process does not provide bipolar structures that can be used effectively. But, as will be shown, bipolar devices can be formed in the CMOS process if additional processing steps are used. The next section describes a modified version of the advanced CMOS process that allows fabrication of bipolar devices.

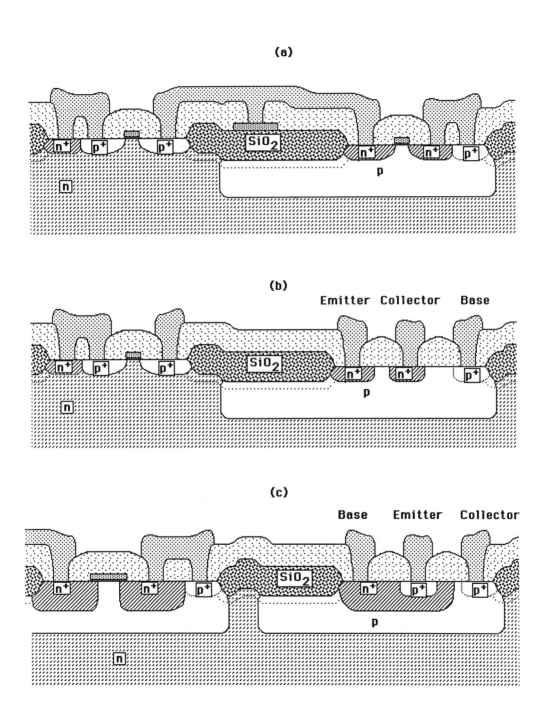

Figure 9-1:   Bipolar transistors in the p-well CMOS process.

9.2. Simple BiMOS process

The process described in this section is "simple" among BiMOS processes but rather advanced among CMOS processes. It uses a low-resistivity substrate, and a lightly doped epitaxial layer to prevent latchup. It also uses the LDD transistor structure and all other enhancements discussed in Chapter 8.

9.2.1. BiMOS technology

The process described in this section employs a heavily doped $<100>$ oriented p-type substrate. In the first steps of the process the substrate is oxidized and photolithography of the buried layer is performed (Fig. 9-2 (a)). The implantation of the buried layer shown in Fig. 9-2 (b) uses a large dose of high-energy As ions. The buried layer implantation is followed by a redistribution step (Fig. 9-2 (c)).

Next a lightly doped p-type epitaxial layer is grown on the surface of the wafer. The epitaxial growth is a high-temperature process and therefore causes further redistribution of the n^+ dopant introduced into the substrate during the buried layer implant (compare Fig. 9-2 (c) and (d)).

The first operation performed on the surface of the epitaxial layer is photolithography of the n-wells, followed by the n-well implantation (Fig. 9-2 (e)). Note that due to the application of the lightly doped epi layer the resistivity of the n-wells can be easily controlled within a large range of values.

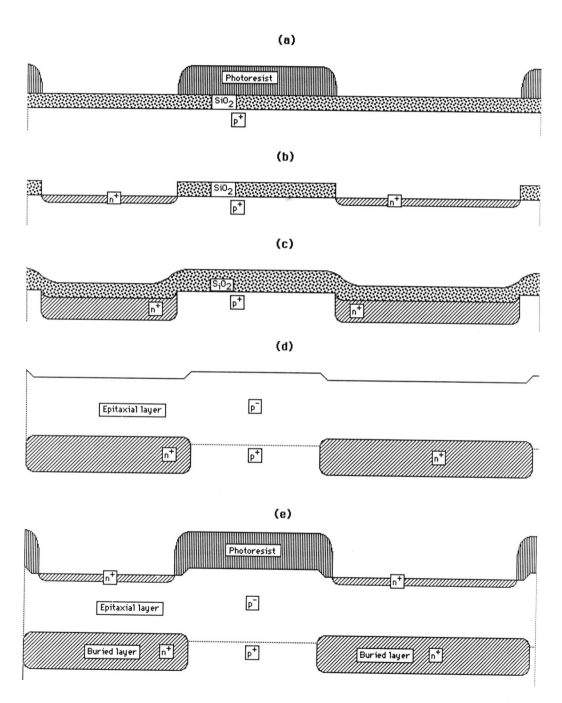

Figure 9-2: BiMOS process. Part I.

After the n-well implant n-well redistribution takes place and both the buried layers and the n-wells penetrate the epitaxial layer (Fig. 9-3 (a)).

Then a typical sequence of steps is performed to create a field oxide. This sequence begins with the deposition of silicon nitride and active region lithography (Fig. 9-3 (b)). The next step is a boron implantation that forms channel-stop regions (Fig. 9-3 (c)). Finally a field oxidation that is also a redistribution of the n-wells and buried layers is performed. After this step the n-wells have been fully formed (Fig. 9-3 (d)) and a gate oxide is grown in the active regions.

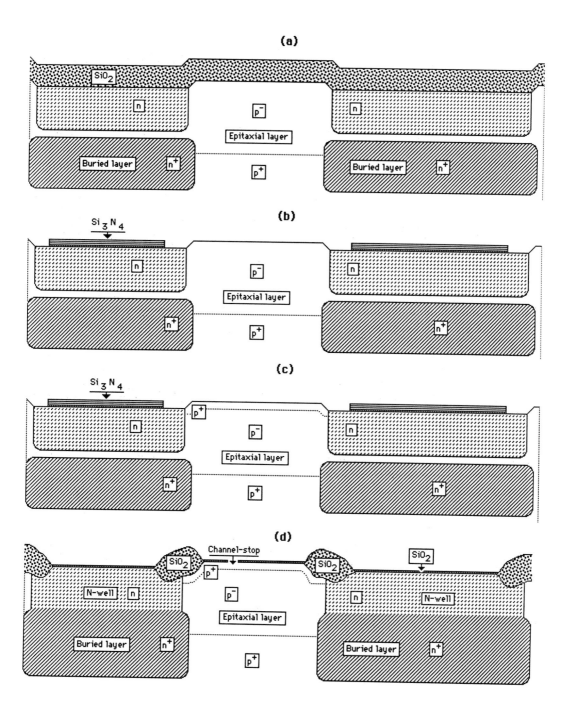

Figure 9-3: BiMOS process. Part II.

In Fig. 9-4(a) the first operation in forming the bipolar transistor is presented. This operation is an implantation of a deep p-type region. It is very crucial for the entire process, because it sets the appropriate threshold voltage of the n-type transistor and it also forms the base of the npn transistor. To meet these requirements this implantation is performed in two steps. First a deep boron implant forming the base is performed and then a shallow threshold adjustment implant is carried out.

After the p-type implants another threshold adjustment implant is performed. It uses phosphorus ions and an appropriate mask to control the threshold voltage of the p-channel transistors (Fig. 9-4 (b)).

The next step is the deposition of phosphorus-doped polysilicon followed by polysilicon lithography (Fig. 9-4 (c)).

(a)

(b)

(c)

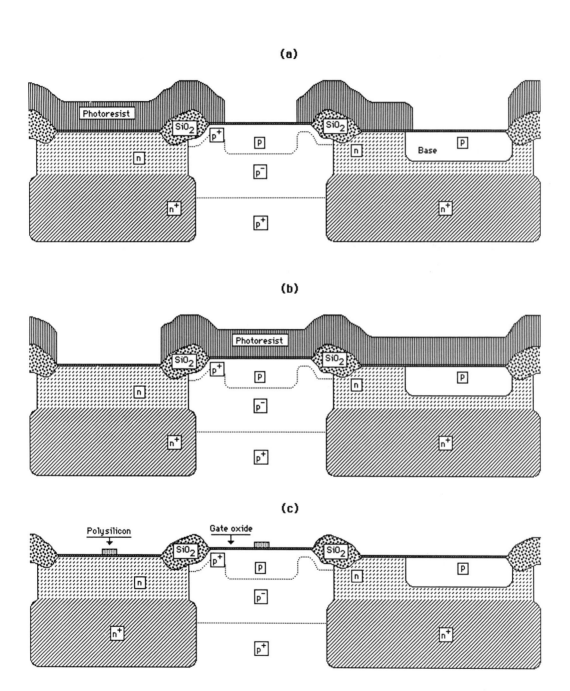

Figure 9-4: BiMOS process. Part III.

Next the LDD structure is created. First, phosphorus ions and the appropriate mask are used to implant the shallow, lightly doped drain and source regions of the n-channel transistors (Fig. 9-5 (a)). Then CVD SiO_2 is deposited on the surface of the wafer (Fig. 9-5 (b)) and is etched to form sidewall spacers. During this etching, the part of the gate oxide that is not covered by sidewall oxide is also removed. Finally, another layer of thin oxide is grown (Fig. 9-5 (c)).

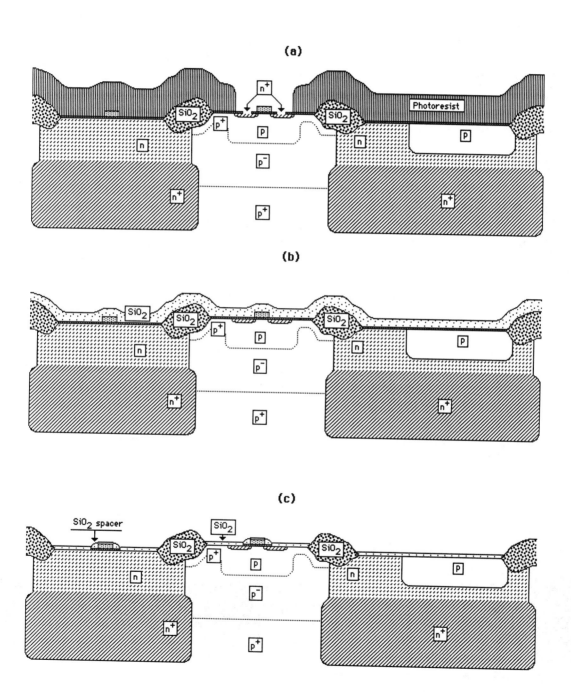

Figure 9-5: BiMOS process. Part IV.

The last step in the formation of the LDD structure is the implantation of arsenic shown in Fig. 9-6 (a). The same implantation is used to build emitters of the npn transistors and contacts to the n-wells. Fig. 9-6 (b) shows the implantation of drains and sources of the p-channel transistors and of contacts to the p-type substrate and the base of the npn transistor. Boron ions are used for this purpose.

The remaining steps of the process are the same as those in the advanced CMOS process described in Chapter 8. They are depicted in Fig. 9-6 (c) and Fig. 9-7. Fig. 9-6 (c) shows the deposition of the LTO SiO_2.

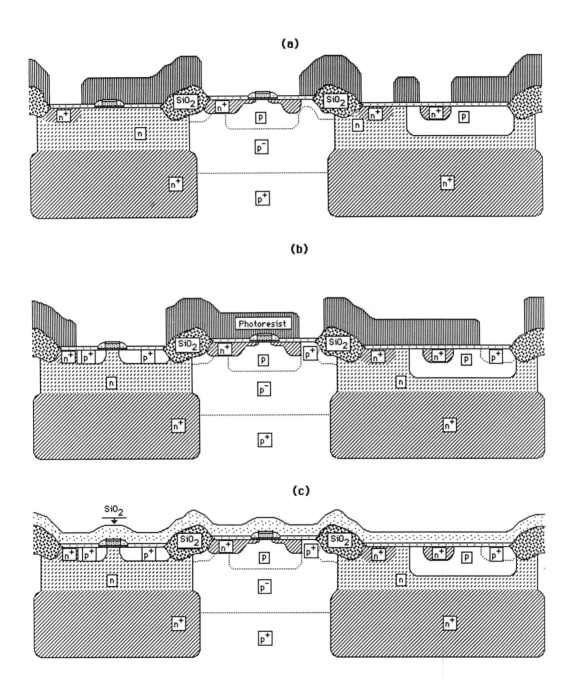

Figure 9-6: BiMOS process. Part V.

Fig. 9-7 (a), (b), and (c) illustrate

- The contact etching step (a);

- The deposition and lithography of the first layer of metal (b); and

- The oxide deposition, planarization, and second metal deposition and lithography (c).

The final step of the process is, as always, deposition of the protective overglass and etching of the windows to the bounding pads.

(a)

(b)

(c)

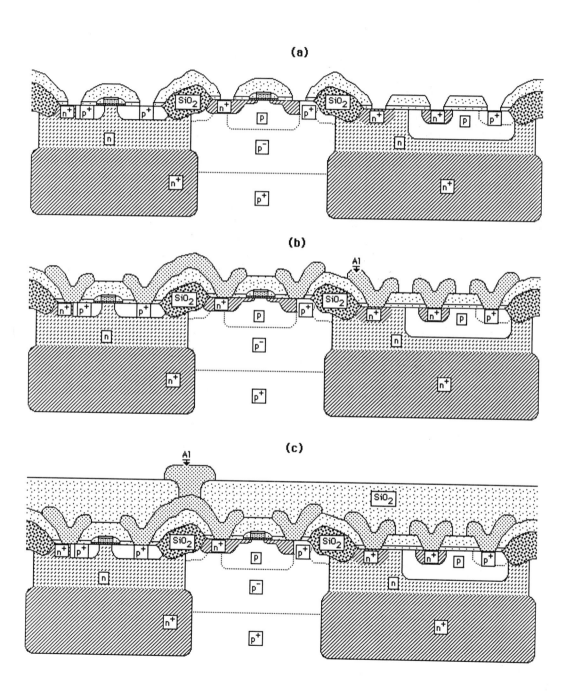

Figure 9-7: BiMOS process. Part VI.

9.2.2. Summary of the features of the elements fabricated with the BiMOS process

Fig. 9-8 summarizes the basic characteristics of the BiMOS process described in this chapter:

- A double level of high-quality metal;

- LDD n-channel transistors;

- Optimal threshold voltages of both the p-channel and the n-channel transistors;

- Effective latchup prevention achieved through the application of a low-resistivity substrate; and

- An optimal vertical npn transistor with an easily controllable β and a low value of the collector series resistance.

An important feature of this process is that the basic electrical parameters of all transistors, MOS and bipolar, can be controlled independently. It is also important that this can be achieved through relatively simple changes in the CMOS process.

Thus, as was demonstrated in this chapter, the CMOS process can be converted into a more complex BiMOS process. Such a change provides the IC designer with a great deal of flexibility. For this reason BiMOS processes may in the future dominate the digital-analog VLSI systems area.

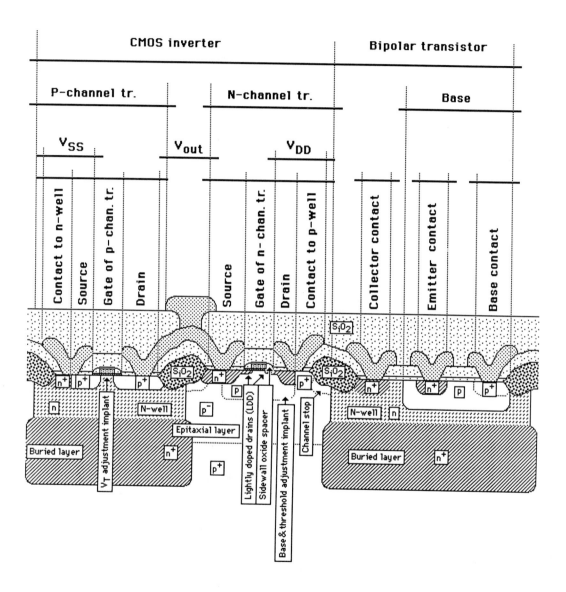

Figure 9-8: Summary of basic features of the BiMOS process.

Chapter 10
Technology of the SRAM

The design and manufacturing of semiconductor memories are among the most difficult and challenging tasks in the entire microelectronics area. This chapter illustrates the complexity of memory design and fabrication, using a **Static Random Access Memory (SRAM)** fabricated in the CMOS technology as an example.

10.1. Trade-offs in memory design and fabrication

Design of semiconductor memories is difficult because of the many crucial design decisions that determine the economical feasibility of memory fabrication. The most important design decision deals with the layout of a single-bit memory cell. The layout of the cell has to be designed in such a way that the fabrication cost, computed per bit of fabricated memories, is minimal.

10.1.1. Layout of the memory cell

The most important characteristic of the memory cell is its size. The size of the cell is determined by its topology and the applied design rules. The designer is able to manipulate the size of the cell by changing the topology of the cell and by applying more relaxed or tighter design rules.

The size of the single-bit memory cell affects manufacturing costs in two ways. A decrease in cell size increases the number of bits that can be fabricated on a die of a given size. Thus, shrinking the cell, attained through clever design or tighter design rules, should assure a lower manufacturing cost per bit of fabricated memory. On the other hand, however, shrinking the memory cell causes an increase in the cell's sensitivity to process fluctuations. Therefore it also causes an increased likelihood that the performance of the cell may be fatally degraded by process instabilities. Consequently, shrinking of the cell increases the fraction of fabricated memories that do not meet needed specifications and thus increases manufacturing cost per bit of fully operational memories.

Hence, an optimal design of the cell is a design that provides the smallest possible size of the cell and at the same time assures low sensitivity to process instabilities. An example of such a design is shown in Fig. 10-1.

A design such as the one shown in Fig. 10-1 is an outcome of years of development and a great deal of designer's experience. Therefore, the drawing shown in Fig. 10-1 should be viewed as the result of an enormous engineering and economic effort. It also represents unusual designer's creativity and thus it can be seen as a piece of "engineering art."

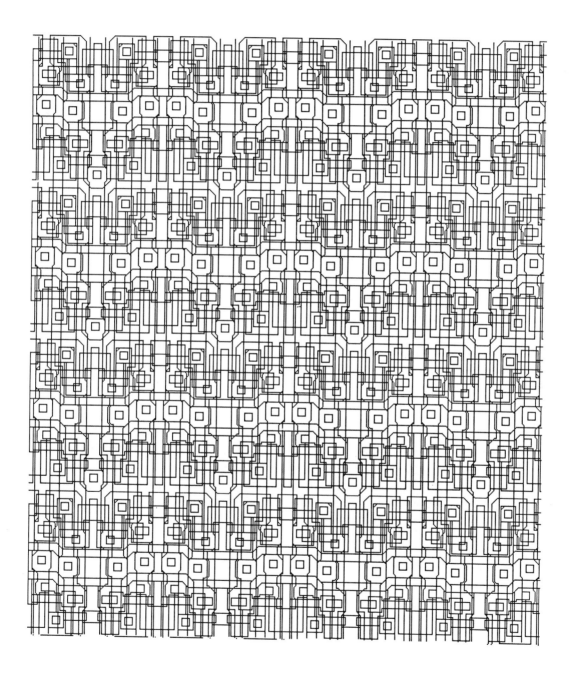

Figure 10-1: Layout of a segment of the SRAM.
The shown segment contains 128 memory cells.

10.1.2. Choice of technology

The size of a single-bit memory cell is optimized not only through creative layout design but also by an appropriate choice of technology. The technology-related trade-offs in memory design can be illustrated well by the following example.

Typically, in a static memory, bistable flip-flops are used to store information. Fig. 10-2 (a) shows a diagram of a typical memory cell composed of six n-channel MOS transistors. Another functionally equivalent version of such a cell is shown in Fig. 10-2 (b). It is composed of four n-channel MOS transistors and two resistors that are used instead of two depletion mode load transistors. Such a substitution is possible and economically justified only when load resistors have a large resistivity and a smaller size than typical load transistors. These conditions can be met when load resistors are made of a very highly resistive material. Usually, a lightly doped polysilicon is used for this purpose. Hence, it is possible to decrease the size of the six-transistor memory, but for this purpose additional processing steps must be used which increase manufacturing cost and affect eventual fabrication cost computed per bit of fabricated memory.

The example of design trade-offs presented above supports a general conclusion that in memory design all aspects of the cell geometry and manufacturing process must be very well understood and carefully optimized. Details of such optimization are outside the scope of this book, but further sections of this chapter illustrate additional elements of the relationship between technology and the geometry of the memory cell.

(a)

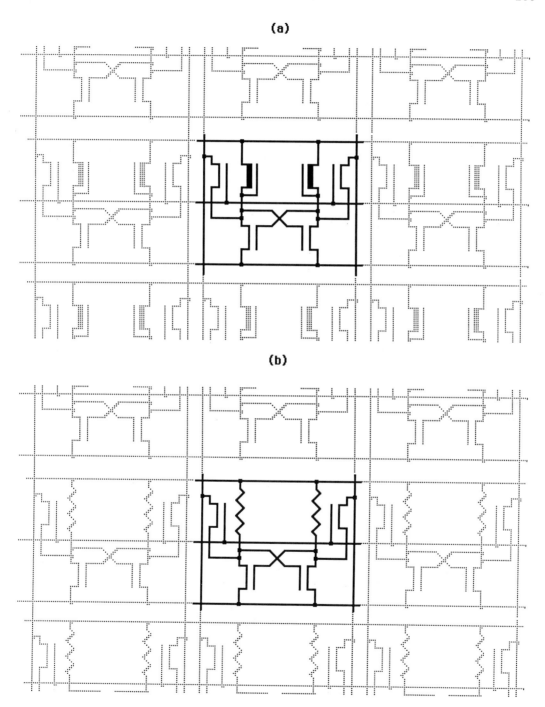

(b)

Figure 10-2: Static RAM memories using six n-channel transistors (a) and four n-channel transistors and two resistors (b).

10.2. Technology of the SRAM

This section presents the technology of a 64K CMOS memory with memory cells such as those depicted in Fig. 10-2 (b). The explanation focuses on the processing steps that form the elements of the cell, i.e. on the n-channel transistors and polysilicon resistors. Therefore, in the further part of this chapter information about processing steps used to create p-channel devices is limited to a minimum. Consequently, all drawings presented in the further part of this chapter show memory elements inside the p-well only.

10.2.1. The SRAM process

The process described in this chapter uses n-type silicon substrate with a $<100>$ orientation. In the first step of this process (not shown in Fig. 10-3), p-wells are created using a p-well mask and a boron high-energy implant. Then the p-type dopant is driven in in an oxidizing atmosphere. After the drive-in the thermal oxide is stripped off and an n-well mask and phosphorus implant are used to form n-wells (also not shown in Fig. 10-3).

In the subsequent steps transistor active areas and channel-stop regions are defined. The typical sequence of operations is used for this purpose. First a layer of silicon nitride is deposited on top of a thin oxide over the entire wafer. Then nitride is patterned using an isolation mask (Fig. 10-3 (a)) and a boron implantation is performed to increase the concentration of p-type dopant in the region that will be covered with the field oxide. Finally, the surface of the wafer unprotected by Si_3N_4 is oxidized using a long high-temperature thermal cycle. After the oxidation the nitride is stripped off.

In the subsequent four steps the transistor gates are formed. The first operation in this sequence is thermal growth of the gate oxide (Fig. 10-3 (d)), followed by the threshold adjustment boron implantation. After implantation the entire wafer is covered with polysilicon referred to as **first polysilicon** (Fig. 10-3 (e)).

An important innovation in the SRAM technology introduces a step that follows polysilicon deposition (see Fig. 10-3 (f)). In this step the entire wafer is covered with a layer of silicide ($TaSi_2$). Silicide is sputtered on to form a low-resistivity connection on top of the medium-resistivity polysilicon.

After silicide sputtering a gate mask is used to define transistor gates (Fig. 10-3 (g)).

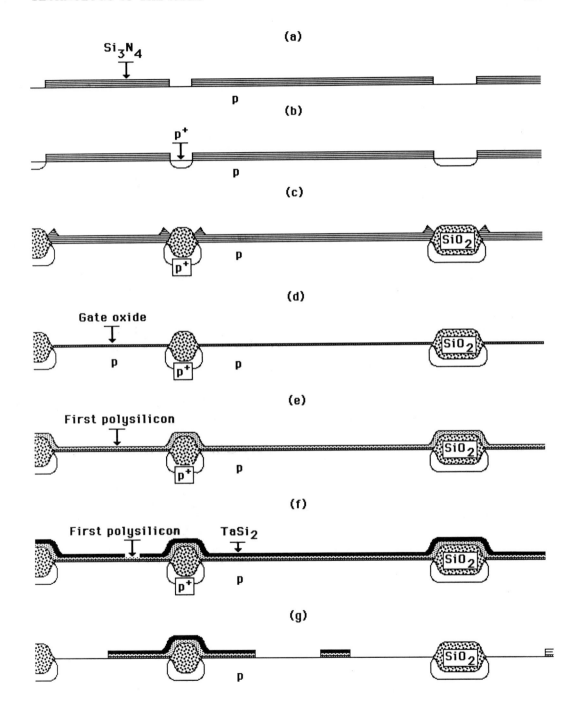

Figure 10-3: SRAM process. Part I.

In the subsequent step (Fig. 10-4 (a)) low pressure chemical vapor deposition (LPCVD) is used to deposit a layer of SiO_2. Then LPCVD oxide is etched (Fig. 10-4 (b)) so that the vertical edges of the silicide-polysilicon sandwich are covered with SiO_2, forming sidewall spacers (for details, see discussion in Chapter 7).

In the next step a phosphorus implant is used to form sources and drains of n-channel transistors. For this purpose an n^+ mask and a layer of photoresist (not shown in Fig. 10-4) are used. After n^+ implantation drains and sources of p-channel transistors are formed. Photoresist and a p^+ mask (not shown in Fig. 10-4) are used during boron implantation to protect regions other than drains and sources of p-channel transistors and contacts to the p-wells.

When the transistors' drains and sources have been created the wafer is covered with LPCVD SiO_2 (Fig. 10-4 (d)) and contact windows to the n^+, p^+, and first polysilicon are etched (Fig. 10-4 (e)).

Then the wafer is covered with undoped (very high-resistivity) polysilicon referred to as **second polysilicon**. Second polysilicon is etched using a subsequent second polysilicon mask.

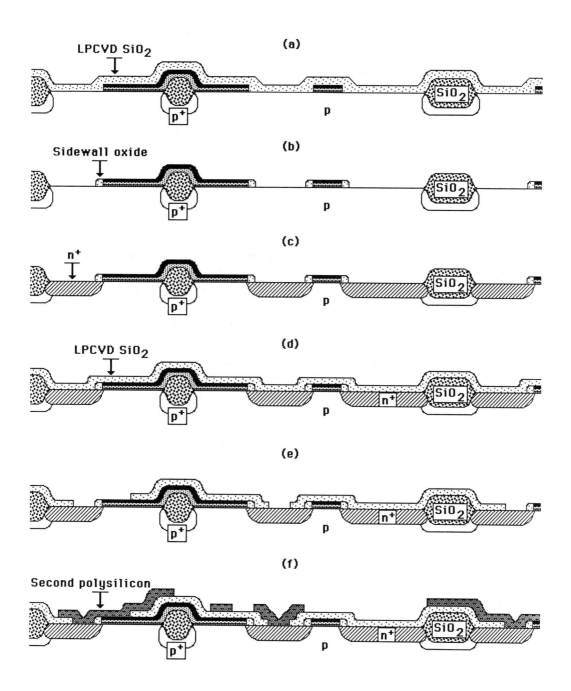

Figure 10-4: SRAM process. Part II.

The second polysilicon is used to create interconnections and large-value resistors. The part of the second polysilicon that will be used for the interconnections must be heavily doped to decrease its resistivity. To achieve this goal, the wafer is thermally oxidized and covered with a layer of silicon nitride (Fig. 10-5 (a)). Then it is patterned in such a way that the nitride is etched from the polysilicon that is supposed to form connections (Fig. 10-5 (b)). At this stage the unprotected second polysilicon can be doped. Two techniques can be used for this purpose: a high-dose, low-energy implantation or predeposition of phosphorus (Fig. 10-5 (c)). Then phosphorus-doped SiO_2 **phosphosilicate glass** (**PSG**) is deposited to isolate the second polysilicon layer from the aluminum layer. A thermal treatment that causes PSG to flow is used to smooth the surface of the wafer.

Following the flow of PSG contact windows are etched (Fig. 10-5 (d)). At this stage contact windows to all conducting layers can be formed.

Finally, aluminum is sputtered over the entire wafer and a metallization mask is used to form metal connections (Fig. 10-5 (e)).

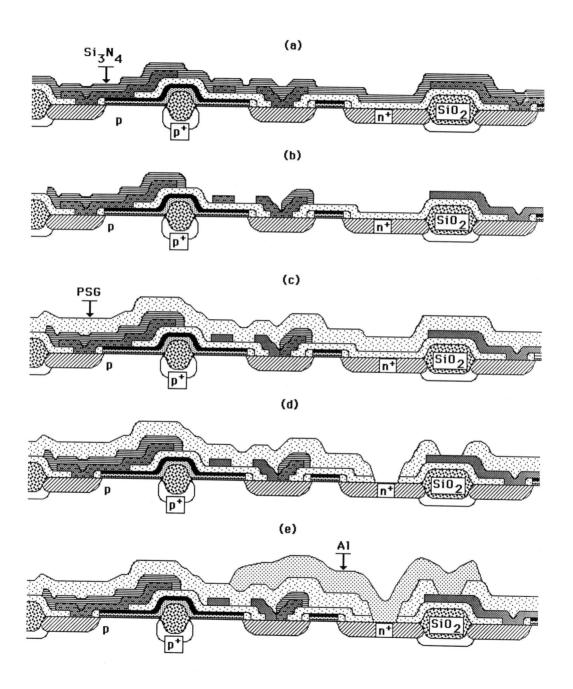

Figure 10-5: SRAM process. Part III.

Fig. 10-6 summarizes the basic features of the process described above.   This
process is capable of creating:

- n-channel and p-channel devices (not shown in Fig. 10-6);

- two layers of polysilicon connections;

- one layer of metal connections; and

- high-resistivity resistors.

The next section shows how the above features are used to create a memory cell.

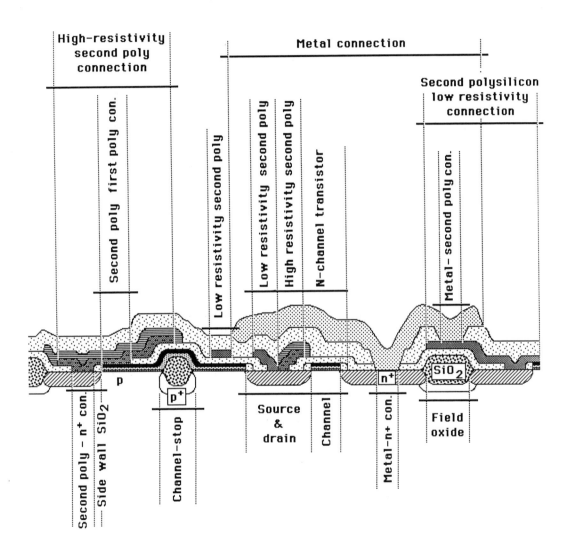

Figure 10-6: Cross-section of a segment of the SRAM cell.

10.2.2. Layout of memory cells

The previous subsection describes the processing steps in the memory fabrication. This subsection explains how these steps are used to create memory cells. For this purpose seven subsequent drawings show seven masks needed to build memory cells. They also illustrate the topology of the surface of the wafer after each lithography step. Each of the drawings depicts an area on which eight memory cells will be created.

The first processing step in which elements of the memory cells are actively patterned is lithography of the isolation (see also Fig. 10-3 (a), (b), and (c)). During this lithography active, channel-stop, and field oxide regions are defined. A top view of the surface of the wafer after nitride stripping is shown in Fig. 10-7. Regions with diagonal shading are open (active regions). White regions are covered with field oxide.

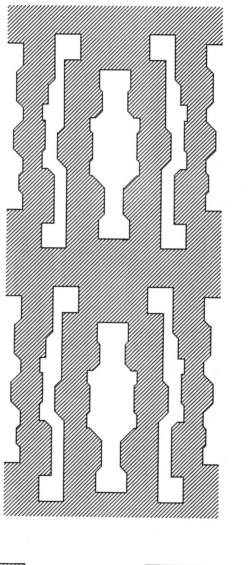

Active region   **Field SiO$_2$**

Figure 10-7: Active region of 8 memory cells.

After gate oxidation and polysilicon and silicide deposition another lithography step is performed with the first polysilicon mask shown in Fig. 10-8 (a). The surface of the wafer after lithography of the first polysilicon layer is shown in Fig. 10-8 (b). Note that the transistor channels are located in the regions where the first polysilicon crosses the active region. Channels of 32 transistors can be seen in Fig. 10-8.

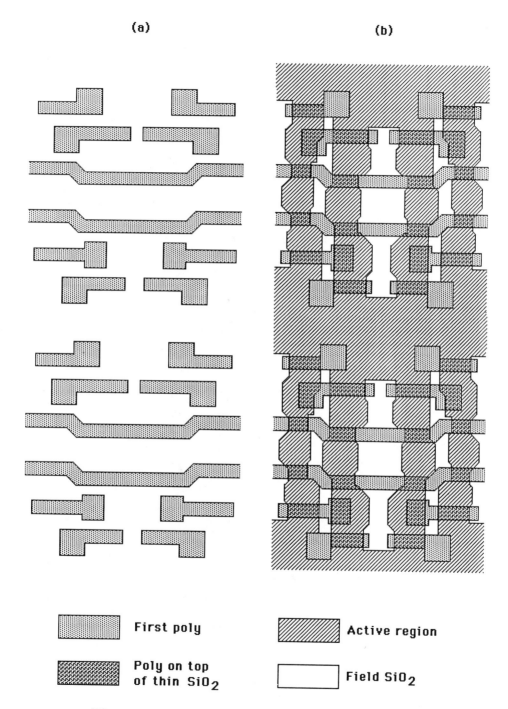

Figure 10-8: The first polysilicon mask (a) and its composition with active region (b). Areas where polysilicon crosses active regions are transistor channels.

The subsequent lithography step is used to form contact windows between active regions and first polysilicon and other connecting layers created later in the process. This step is performed after sidewall oxide formation and LPCVD deposition (see steps in Fig. 10-4). The first contacts mask is shown in Fig. 10-9 (a) and its composition with the layout features created in the previous processing steps is depicted in Fig. 10-9 (b). Note and remember the segments of the windows that open SiO_2 to the substrate and first polysilicon.

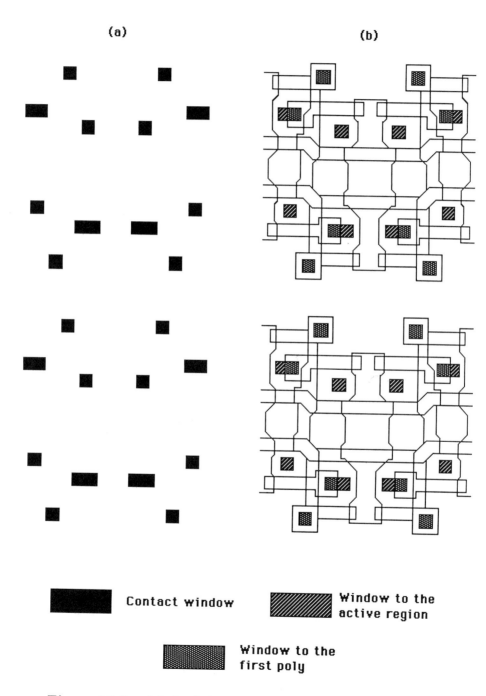

Figure 10-9: Mask of the contact cuts in the LTO oxide (a). Cuts are created to the first polysilicon and the substrate (b).

In the next lithography step the second (highly resistive) polysilicon layer is patterned, using the second polysilicon mask shown in Fig. 10-10 (a).   The topology of the surface of the wafer after the second polysilicon lithography is shown in Fig. 10-10 (b). Note that in some of the contact windows second polysilicon connects the first polysilicon with the n^+ source and drain regions.

(a)

(b)

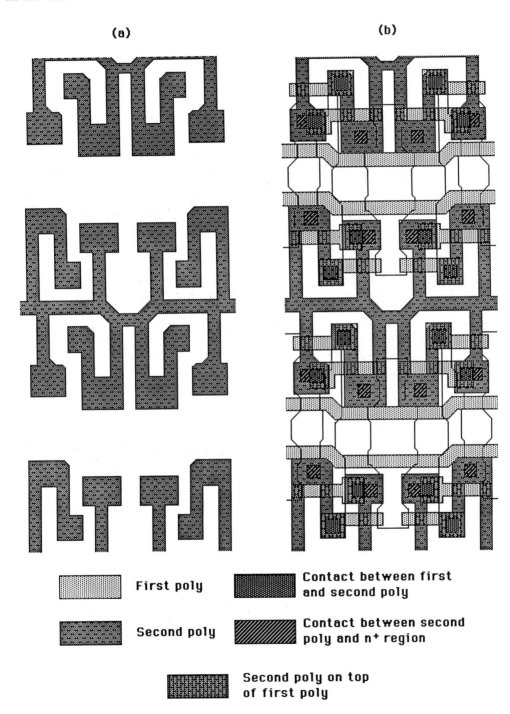

First poly

Second poly

Contact between first
and second poly

Contact between second
poly and n⁺ region

Second poly on top
of first poly

Figure 10-10: Second polysilicon mask (a) and composition of
the first and second polysilicon layers (b).

The subsequent mask shown in Fig. 10-11 (a) and referred to as the **load resistor mask** is used to etch a silicon nitride layer deposited on the surface of the wafer. Regions unprotected by the nitride (see also Fig. 10-5 (b) and (c)) will be doped with phosphorus. In Fig. 10-11 (a) the regions of the mask that indicate protected areas of the wafer surface are filled with horizontal lines. Hence, segments of the second polysilicon connections that are doped with phosphorus and thus form low-resistance connections are marked in Fig. 10-11 with new (gray) shading.

(a)   (b)

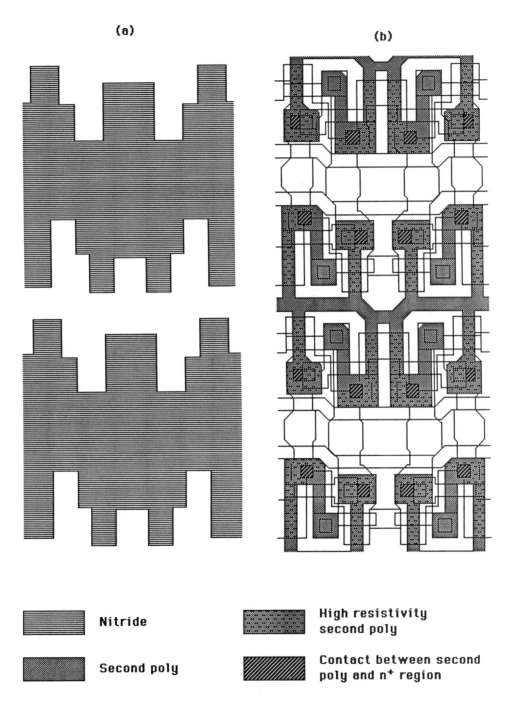

Nitride

Second poly

High resistivity
second poly

Contact between second
poly and n+ region

Figure 10-11: Load resistor mask (a) and doped
and undoped second polysilicon regions (b).

After the resistor load lithography standard masks are used. First a typical contact window mask (Fig. 10-12 (a)) is used to open the layers of SiO_2 in the locations where metal connections to other conducting layers will be created. As indicated in Fig. 10-12 (b), such connections are made to the n^+ regions.

(a) **(b)**

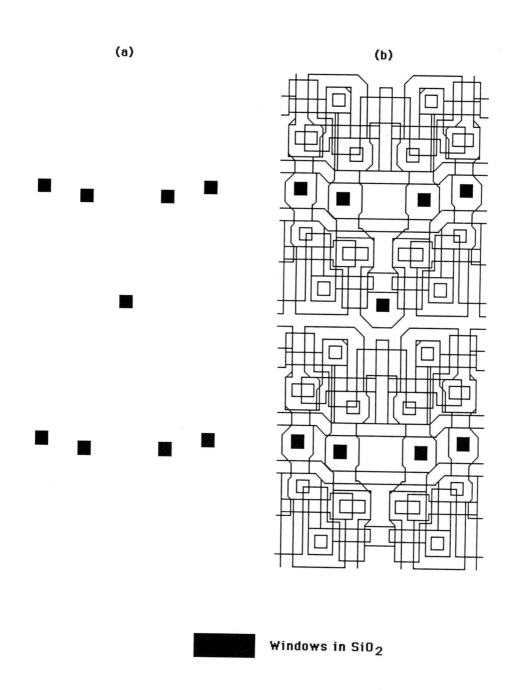

Windows in SiO$_2$

Figure 10-12: Mask of contact cuts in the oxide layers (a) and composite layout with contact cuts to the n$^+$ regions (b).

The last mask forming the layout of the memory cells is the metallization mask shown in Fig. 10-13 (a). The surface of the wafer after the metallization lithography is depicted in Fig. 10-13 (b).

Note that the drawing of the surface of the wafer shown in Fig. 10-13 (b) forms the pattern that was used to draw the picture shown in Fig. 10-1.

(a)   **(b)**

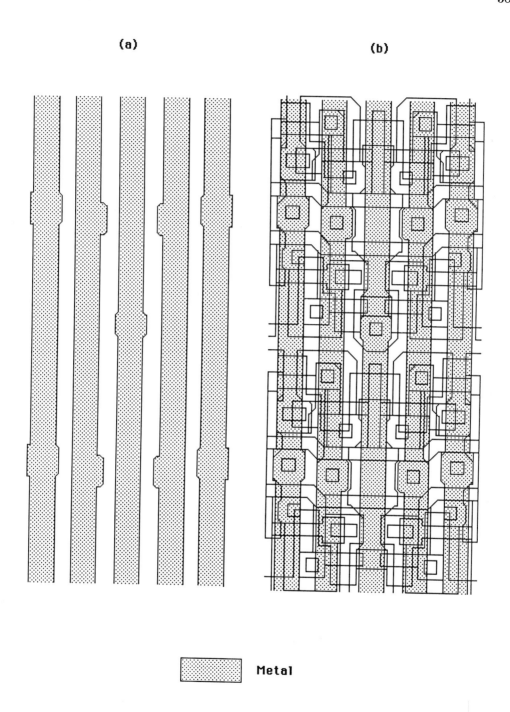

▒▒▒▒▒ **Metal**

Figure 10-13: Metal layer mask (a) and composition of the metal layer with
outlines of all other layers (b) shown.

10.2.3. Electrical diagram of a single-bit memory cell

The drawing shown in Fig. 10-14 uses a solid-line box to represent one segment of the memory that contains eight memory cells. In this subsection the electrical diagram of such a single-bit cell is discussed. To interpret the layout of the single-bit memory cell it is necessary to know that:

- Metal lines are used to carry single-bit signals and the central line is used as a ground.

- V_{cc} is distributed by second polysilicon horizontal lines.

- Word lines are formed in the first polysilicon layer.

Between these lines eight memory cells are arranged. Each of these cells is a rotation or mirror image of the same cell.

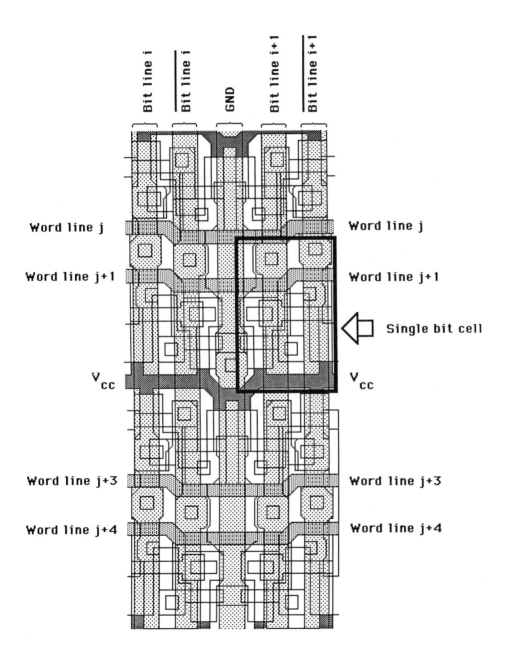

Figure 10-14: Complete layout of the 8-bit segment of the SRAM memory with highlighted word, bit, ground, and V_{cc} lines.

Fig. 10-15 explains details of the single memory cell. Note four transistor channel regions in Fig. 10-15 (a). Note also that high-resistivity segments of the second polysilicon connect the V_{cc} line and the n^+ regions that are drains of the transistors controlled by the word line (Fig. 10-15 (a) and (b)). Sources of these transistors are connected to the vertical metal lines (Fig. 10-15 (c)).

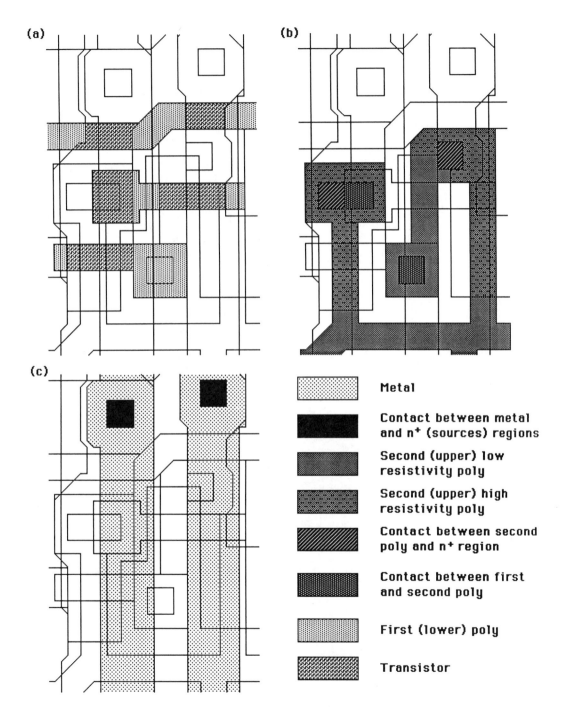

Figure 10-15:   Basic layers in the single-bit memory cell.
First polysilicon (a), second polysilicon
with high resistivity areas (b), and metal
layer (c).

Fig. 10-16 reveals other details of the single memory cell. A perspective view depicted in Fig. 10-16 (a) shows all conducting layers of the cell. Arrows indicate electrical connections between layers. Fig. 10-16 (b) presents the electrical diagram extracted from Fig. 10-16 (a). The diagram from Fig. 10-16 (b) redrawn in the conventional way is shown in Fig. 10-16 (c).

Hence, the memory cell analyzed in this section has exactly the same diagram as the diagram shown in Fig. 10-2. Of course, all other cells in the segment of the layout depicted in Fig. 10-14 are the same. So, it seems obvious now that the drawing shown at the beginning of this chapter (Fig. 10-1) represents the layout of 128 bistable flip-flops that form a segment of a 64K static random access memory that uses polysilicon resistors as load devices.

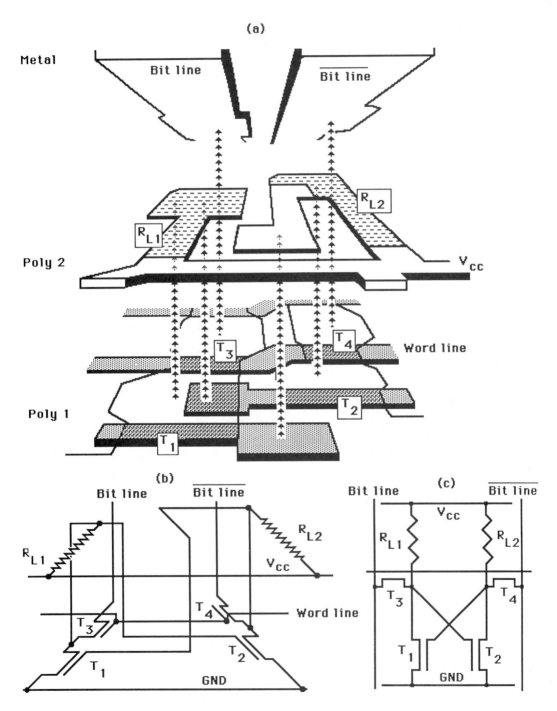

Figure 10-16: Electrical diagram of a single memory cell.
Composition of the basic layers (a), electrical
diagram extracted from the composition of the
basic layers (b), and schematic of the cell (c).

10.3. Scanning Electron Microscope photos

This section illustrates the previously discussed SRAM manufacturing process with **Scanning Electron Microscope (SEM)** photographs. The photographs presented in this section were taken from segments of manufacturing wafers after major manufacturing steps. On each of the following pages two pictures are presented; one showing the surface of the wafer with one memory cell and a second showing the surface of the wafer with four cells. The photographs should be self-explanatory and the reader should be able to identify the objects shown and to relate them to the drawings presented in Fig. 10-2 through Fig. 10-14. The last three figures of this section show SEM photos of the cross-sections of the memory cell. They seem to be self-explanatory as well and the reader should be able to identify all the layers in the pictures and the locations in the memory cell where the cross-sectional cuts were performed.

Finally, it must be stressed that this section seems to be one of the most important sections of this book and should be very carefully studied. It is important not only because it illustrates a complicated process with actual images but also because it reveals differences between various "idealized" drawings of the memory cells and actual photographs of the memory cell. The reader is strongly encouraged to study these differences and to relate them to the information presented in Chapter 2.

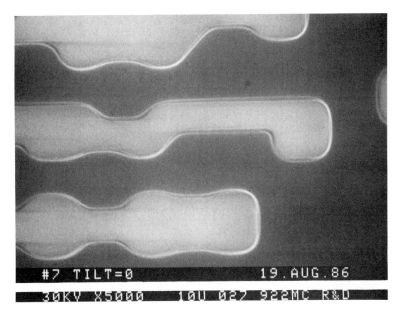

Figure 10-17:   SEM photo of the surface of the manufacturing
wafer covering 1 memory cell after active region lithography.
Courtesy of Fairchild Semiconductor Research Center.

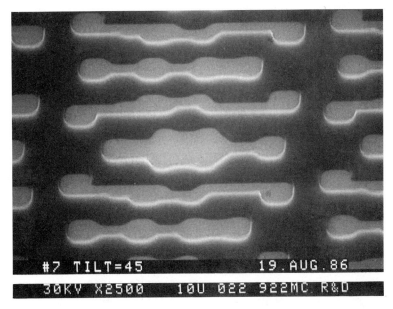

Figure 10-18:   SEM photo of the surface of the manufacturing wafer
covering 4 memory cells after lithography of the active region.
Courtesy of Fairchild Semiconductor Research Center.

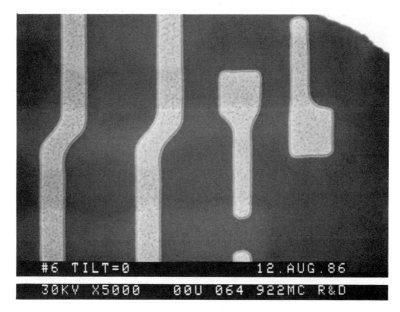

Figure 10-19: SEM photo of the surface of the manufacturing wafer covering 1 memory cell after lithography of the first polysilicon.
Courtesy of Fairchild Semiconductor Research Center.

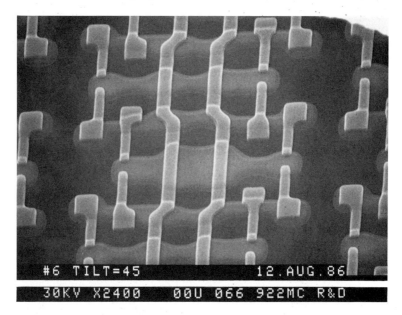

Figure 10-20: SEM photo of the surface of the manufacturing wafer covering 4 memory cells after lithography of the first polysilicon.
Courtesy of Fairchild Semiconductor Research Center.

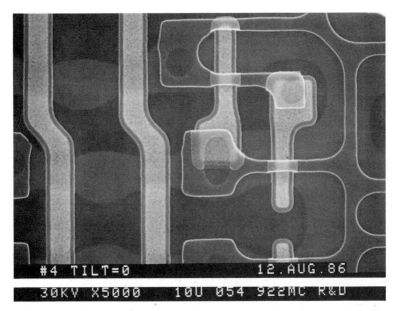

Figure 10-21: SEM photo of the surface of the manufacturing wafer covering 1 memory cell after lithography of contact cuts in the LTO and second polysilicon.
Courtesy of Fairchild Semiconductor Research Center.

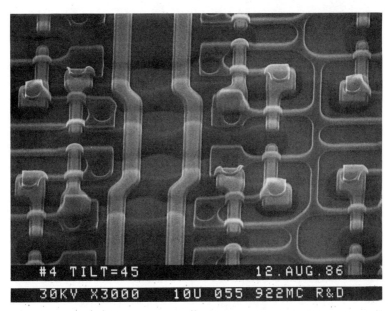

Figure 10-22: SEM photo of the surface of the manufacturing wafer covering 4 memory cells after lithography of contact cuts in the LTO and second polysilicon.
Courtesy of Fairchild Semiconductor Research Center.

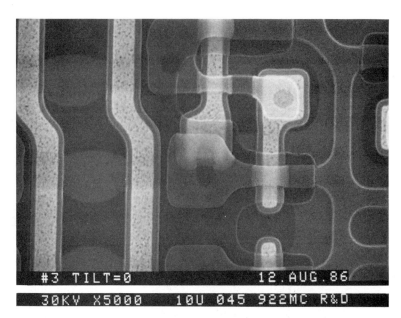

Figure 10-23:   SEM photo of the surface of the manufacturing wafer
covering 1 memory cell after load resistor nitride etching.
Courtesy of Fairchild Semiconductor Research Center.

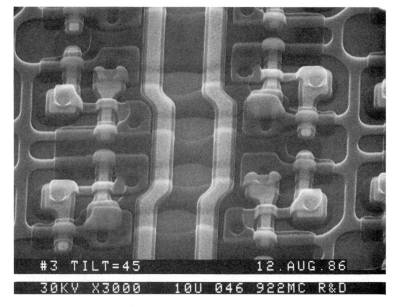

Figure 10-24:   SEM photo of the surface of the manufacturing wafer
covering 4 memory cells after load resistor nitride etching.
Courtesy of Fairchild Semiconductor Research Center.

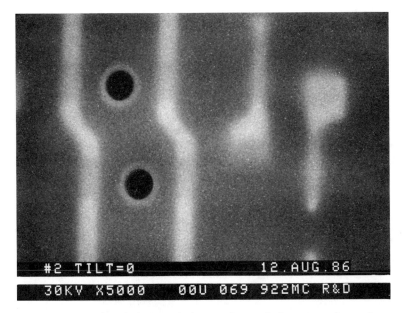

Figure 10-25: SEM photo of the surface of the manufacturing wafer covering 1 memory cell after etching of the contact cuts. *Courtesy of Fairchild Semiconductor Research Center.*

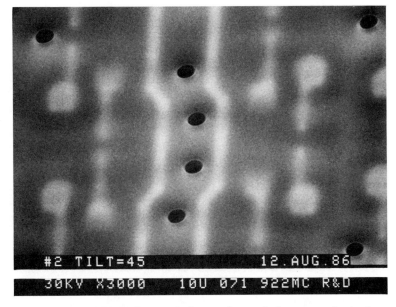

Figure 10-26: SEM photo of the surface of the manufacturing wafer covering 4 memory cells after etching of the contact cuts. *Courtesy of Fairchild Semiconductor Research Center.*

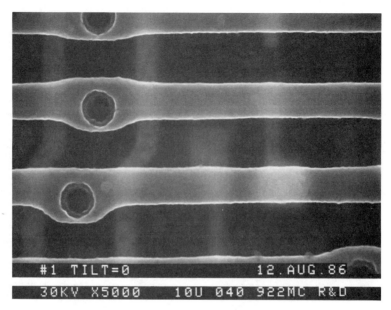

Figure 10-27: SEM photo of the surface of the manufacturing wafer
covering 1 memory cell after metallization.
Courtesy of Fairchild Semiconductor Research Center.

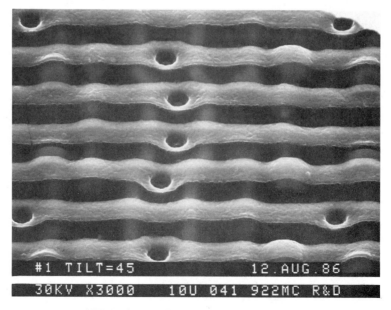

Figure 10-28: SEM photo of the surface of the manufacturing wafer
covering 4 memory cells after metallization.
Courtesy of Fairchild Semiconductor Research Center.

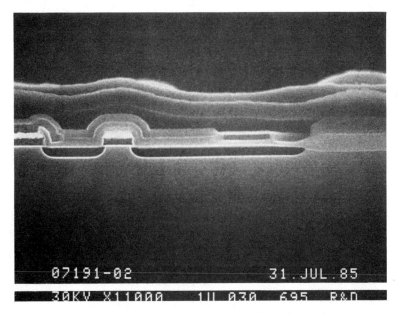

Figure 10-29: SEM photo of the cross-section through 1 memory cell. *Courtesy of Fairchild Semiconductor Research Center.*

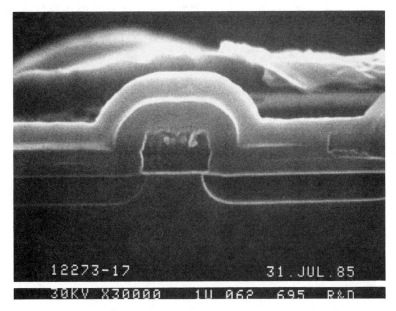

Figure 10-30: SEM photo of the cross-section through a transistor. *Courtesy of Fairchild Semiconductor Research Center.*

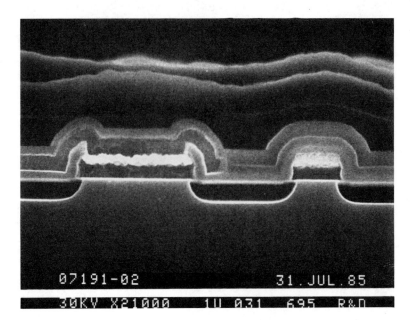

Figure 10-31: SEM photo of the cross-section through a
transistor and first and second polysilicon contact.
Courtesy of Fairchild Semiconductor Research Center.

Chapter 11
Silicon - on - Insulator Technology

with contributions from
Jerzy Ruzyllo

For the minimization of the electrical interaction between components of an integrated circuit, such as latchup or other parasitic phenomena, an effective isolation between IC elements is very crucial.

This issue is particularly critical for the performance of the most advanced circuits. In order to achieve high packing density in these circuits, the separation between components must be very small and the isolation problem is inherently magnified. An attractive approach in this domain is offered by the **Silicon - on - Insulator (SOI)** technology which will be introduced briefly in this chapter.

11.1. Basic concept of the SOI technology

The substrate used in conventional bulk silicon technology is a mechanically coherent wafer of single-crystal silicon, several hundreds of micrometers thick. In the SOI technology, all features of the IC layout are processed into a thin film, usually thinner than one micrometer, of single-crystal silicon that is deposited on an insulator. Such a configuration allows etching of trenches in the silicon down to the insulator and thus the creation of separate isolated islands of crystalline silicon for each individual component of the IC.

Fig. 11-1 summarizes the basic concept of the SOI technology using the above-mentioned idea. In this technology a thin layer of Si is grown on the surface of, for instance, sapphire (Fig. 11-1 (a)). Then trenches are etched (Fig. 11-1 (b)). To form p-channel and n-channel transistors the silicon islands have to be doped with a p-type dopant (Fig. 11-1 (c)), which is achieved with the appropriate implantation step. Next, as in the traditional process the gate oxide growth and polysilicon deposition have to be carried out (Fig. 11-1 (d)). In the following steps implants can be used to form the drains and sources of both the p-channel and the n-channel devices (Fig. 11-1 (e) and (f)). Finally a layer of SiO_2 is deposited and standard contact and metallization lithographies are performed. The resulting structure is shown in Fig. 11-1 (g).

The main advantages of SOI technology include:

- Improved density due to the small area covered by the isolation;

- Improved lateral isolation which in the case of CMOS circuits results in the elimination of the latchup problem; and

- Reduced parasitic capacitances compared to other isolation techniques.

These advantages make SOI technology very suitable for high-speed IC manufacturing. In addition, SOI technology enables the implementation of three-dimensional IC's, which are expected to solve many of the problems limiting further expansion of today's two-dimensional IC's.

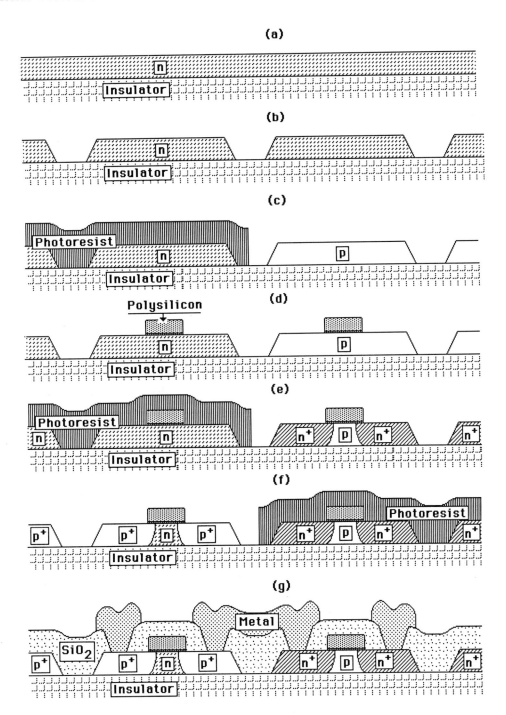

Figure 11-1: Basic concept of the SOI process.

11.2. Various SOI technologies

All SOI technologies fall into two broad categories that can be distinguished on the basis of the type of insulator used as a substrate. The type of insulator in turn determines the technique applied to fabricate a thin film of single-crystal silicon on top of it.

In the first approach, an insulator acting as a substrate is selected to match the crystallographic structure of silicon as closely as possible. Having such a substrate, the thin film of single-crystal silicon can be deposited by means of epitaxy. The insulator most commonly used for this purpose is sapphire, and thus **Silicon-on-Sapphire (SOS)** technology is the most representative for this category of SOI implementation (Fig. 11-2 (a)). Shortcomings of SOS technology result from an imperfect matching of the crystal lattice of silicon with the sapphire, which results in a relatively high number of defects in the epitaxial silicon. The significantly different thermal expansion coefficients of silicon and sapphire are also of concern in practical applications of SOS technology.

In the second approach, the "active" thin film of single-crystal silicon is processed onto the layer of amorphous silicon dioxide or silicon nitride, which has been formed on the surface of the conventional Si wafer. The various techniques that can be used to obtain a layer of single-crystal silicon in this configuration include:

- Recrystallization of the amorphous or polycrystalline silicon deposited on SiO_2 to the single-crystal form. Most commonly, a laser beam is used for this purpose, and the single-crystal silicon from the substrate wafer acts as a seed that sets a crystallographic pattern to be reproduced throughout the thin silicon film during the recrystallization (Fig. 11-2 (b)).

- Formation of a buried SiO_2 layer by ion implantation (Fig. 11-2 (c)). In this case, oxygen ions are implanted through the surface region of the single-crystal silicon wafer to form an oxide layer underneath it. The dose and energy of the ion beam can be adjusted to control the width and depth of the oxide layer.

- Lateral epitaxial overgrowth (Fig. 11-2 (d)) in which the epitaxial deposition of silicon first takes place at the seed region. When the growing silicon layer becomes thicker than the oxide layer, lateral overgrowth of single-crystal silicon is allowed.

These and other techniques of SOI structures fabrication are extensively studied, and it is difficult to determine at this time which one will play a dominant role in future practical applications.

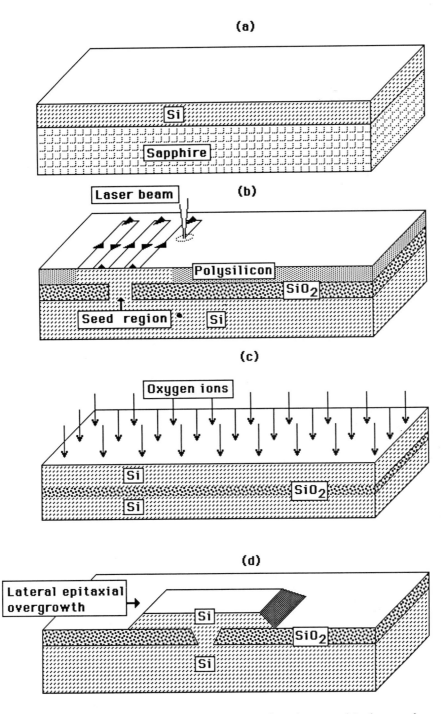

Figure 11-2: Various techniques used to form a thin layer of single-crystal Si on top of the insulator.

Appendix I
Further Readings

Since it was assumed that this Atlas should be a visual introduction to VLSI processes, the verbal component of the information presented was kept to the minimum. Therefore, descriptions of IC technologies that actually may be composed of thousands of pages had to be drastically condensed. The discussion of the device and process physics was also limited to the basics or skipped altogether. Thus, the reader who wishes to learn about some of the aspects of VLSI circuits and processes should study other sources. This Appendix suggests some sources that may be useful for this purpose.

Circuit and device-related aspects of IC are discussed in:

P. M. Chirlian, *Analysis and Design of Integrated Circuits*, Harper & Row Publishers, New York, 1987.

P. R. Gray and R. G. Meyer, *Analysis and Design of Analog Integrated Circuits*, John Wiley & Sons, New York, 1977.

D. A. Hodges and H. G. Jackson, *Analysis and Design of Digital Integrated Circuits*, McGraw-Hill Book Company, New York, 1983.

J. Millman and A. Grabel, *Microelectronics*, McGraw-Hill Book Company, New York, 1987.

C. J. Savant, M. S. Roden, and G. L. Carpenter, *Electronic Circuit Design*, The Benjamin/Cummings Publishing Company, Inc., 1987.

Texts dealing with circuit and system aspects of VLSI circuits are:

M. Annaratone, *Digital CMOS Circuit Design*, Kluwer Academic Publishers, Boston, 1986.

L. A. Glasser and D. W. Dobberpuhl, *The Design and Analysis of VLSI Circuits*, Addison-Wesley Publishing Company, 1985.

J. Mavor, M. A. Jack, and P. B. Denyer, *Introduction to MOS LSI Design*, Addison-Wesley Publishing Company, London, 1983.

C. Mead and L. Conway, *Introduction to VLSI Systems*. Addison-Wesley Publishing Co., 1980.

N. Weste and K. Eshraghian, *Principles of CMOS VLSI Design - A System Perspective*, Addison-Wesley Publishing Company, 1985.

The physics of the processes and details of the processing steps are discussed in:

R. A. Colclaser, *Microelectronics: Processing and Device Design*, John Wiley & Sons, New York, 1980.

S. K. Ghandi, *VLSI Fabrication Principles*, John Wiley & Sons, New York, 1983.

W. S. Ruska, *Microelectronics Processing: An Introduction to the Manufacture of Integrated Circuits*, McGraw-Hill Book Company, New York 1987.

S. M. Sze, *VLSI Technology*, McGraw-Hill Book Company, New York, 1983.

S. Wolff and R. N. Tauber, *Silicon Processing for the VLSI Era*, Volume 1, Lattice Press, 1986.

Traditional but still very useful sources of information about bipolar ICs are:

D. J. Hamilton and W. G. Howard, *Basic Integrated Circuit Engineering*, McGraw-Hill Book Company, New York, 1975.

A. B. Glaser and G. E. Subak-Sharpe, *Integrated Circuit Engineering*, Addison-Wesley Publishing Company, Reading, Massachusetts, 1977.

M. I. Elmasry, *Digital Bipolar Integrated Circuits*, John Wiley & Sons, New York, 1983.

Finally, descriptions of the advanced processes can be found in:

D. J. McGreivy and K. A. Pickar (Editors), *VLSI Technologies Through the 80s and Beyond*, IEEE Computer Society Press, New York, 1982.

IEEE Journal of Solid-State Circuits, *Joint Special Issue on Very Large Scale of Integration*, February, 1985, Volume SC-20.

Proceedings of *IEEE International Solid-State Circuit Conference*.

Proceedings of *IEEE International Electron Device Meeting*.

It has to be stressed, however, that complete process descriptions are very rarely published and that details about advanced VLSI processes are not available in the literature.

Index